OFFICIAL SQA PAST PAPERS WITH ANSWERS

HIGHER

PHYSICS
2009-2013

Hodder Gibson is grateful to the copyright holders, as credited on the final page of the Question Section, for permission to use their material. Every effort has been made to trace the copyright holders and to obtain their permission for the use of copyright material. Hodder Gibson will be happy to receive information allowing us to rectify any error or omission in future editions.

Hachette UK's policy is to use papers that are natural, renewable and recyclable products and made from wood grown in sustainable forests. The logging and manufacturing processes are expected to conform to the environmental regulations of the country of origin.

Orders: please contact Bookpoint Ltd, 130 Park Drive, Abingdon, Oxon OX14 4SE. Telephone: (44) 01235 827720. Fax: (44) 01235 400454.

Lines are open 9.00–5.00, Monday to Saturday, with a 24-hour message answering service. Visit our website at www.hoddereducation.co.uk. Hodder Gibson can be contacted direct on: Tel: 0141 848 1609; Fax: 0141 889 6315; email: hoddergibson@hodder.co.uk

This collection first published in 2013 by

Hodder Gibson, an imprint of Hodder Education,

An Hachette UK Company

2a Christie Street

Paisley PA1 1NB

BrightRED Hodder Gibson is grateful to Bright Red Publishing Ltd for collaborative work in preparation of this book and all
PUBLISHING SQA Past Paper and National 5 Model Paper titles 2013.

Typeset by PDQ Digital Media Solutions Ltd, Bungay, Suffolk NR35 1BY

Printed in the UK

A catalogue record for this title is available from the British Library

ISBN 978-1-4718-0297-3

3 2 1

2014 2013

Introduction
Study Skills – what you need to know to pass exams!

Pause for thought

Many students might skip quickly through a page like this. After all, we all know how to revise. Do you really though?

Think about this:

"IF YOU ALWAYS DO WHAT YOU ALWAYS DO, YOU WILL ALWAYS GET WHAT YOU HAVE ALWAYS GOT."

Do you like the grades you get? Do you want to do better? If you get full marks in your assessment, then that's great! Change nothing! This section is just to help you get that little bit better than you already are.

There are two main parts to the advice on offer here. The first part highlights fairly obvious things but which are also very important. The second part makes suggestions about revision that you might not have thought about but which WILL help you.

Part 1

DOH! It's so obvious but …

Start revising in good time

Don't leave it until the last minute – this will make you panic.

Make a revision timetable that sets out work time AND play time.

Sleep and eat!

Obvious really, and very helpful. Avoid arguments or stressful things too – even games that wind you up. You need to be fit, awake and focused!

Know your place!

Make sure you know exactly **WHEN and WHERE** your exams are.

Know your enemy!

Make sure you know what to expect in the exam.

How is the paper structured?

How much time is there for each question?

What types of question are involved?

Which topics seem to come up time and time again?

Which topics are your strongest and which are your weakest?

Are all topics compulsory or are there choices?

Learn by DOING!

There is no substitute for past papers and practice papers – they are simply essential! Tackling this collection of papers and answers is exactly the right thing to be doing as your exams approach.

Part 2

People learn in different ways. Some like low light, some bright. Some like early morning, some like evening / night. Some prefer warm, some prefer cold. But everyone uses their BRAIN and the brain works when it is active. Passive learning – sitting gazing at notes – is the most INEFFICIENT way to learn anything. Below you will find tips and ideas for making your revision more effective and maybe even more enjoyable. What follows gets your brain active, and active learning works!

Activity 1 – Stop and review

Step 1

When you have done no more than 5 minutes of revision reading STOP!

Step 2

Write a heading in your own words which sums up the topic you have been revising.

Step 3

Write a summary of what you have revised in no more than two sentences. Don't fool yourself by saying, 'I know it but I cannot put it into words'. That just means you don't know it well enough. If you cannot write your summary, revise that section again, knowing that you must write a summary at the end of it. Many of you will have notebooks full of blue/black ink writing. Many of the pages will not be especially attractive or memorable so try to liven them up a bit with colour as you are reviewing and rewriting. **This is a great memory aid, and memory is the most important thing.**

Activity 2 — Use technology!

Why should everything be written down? Have you thought about 'mental' maps, diagrams, cartoons and colour to help you learn? And rather than write down notes, why not record your revision material?

What about having a text message revision session with friends? Keep in touch with them to find out how and what they are revising and share ideas and questions.

Why not make a video diary where you tell the camera what you are doing, what you think you have learned and what you still have to do? No one has to see or hear it but the process of having to organise your thoughts in a formal way to explain something is a very important learning practice.

Be sure to make use of electronic files. You could begin to summarise your class notes. Your typing might be slow but it will get faster and the typed notes will be easier to read than the scribbles in your class notes. Try to add different fonts and colours to make your work stand out. You can easily Google relevant pictures, cartoons and diagrams which you can copy and paste to make your work more attractive and **MEMORABLE**.

Activity 3 – This is it. Do this and you will know lots!

Step 1

In this task you must be very honest with yourself! Find the SQA syllabus for your subject (www.sqa.org.uk). Look at how it is broken down into main topics called MANDATORY knowledge. That means stuff you MUST know.

Step 2

BEFORE you do ANY revision on this topic, write a list of everything that you already know about the subject. It might be quite a long list but you only need to write it once. It shows you all the information that is already in your long-term memory so you know what parts you do not need to revise!

Step 3

Pick a chapter or section from your book or revision notes. Choose a fairly large section or a whole chapter to get the most out of this activity.

With a buddy, use Skype, Facetime, Twitter or any other communication you have, to play the game "If this is the answer, what is the question?". For example, if you are revising Geography and the answer you provide is "meander", your buddy would have to make up a question like "What is the word that describes a feature of a river where it flows slowly and bends often from side to side?".

Make up 10 "answers" based on the content of the chapter or section you are using. Give this to your buddy to solve while you solve theirs.

Step 4

Construct a wordsearch of at least 10 X 10 squares. You can make it as big as you like but keep it realistic. Work together with a group of friends. Many apps allow you to make wordsearch puzzles online. The words and phrases can go in any direction and phrases can be split. Your puzzle must only contain facts linked to the topic you are revising. Your task is to find 10 bits of information to hide in your puzzle but you must not repeat information that you used in Step 3. DO NOT show where the words are. Fill up empty squares with random letters. Remember to keep a note of where your answers are hidden but do not show your friends. When you have a complete puzzle, exchange it with a friend to solve each other's puzzle.

Step 5

Now make up 10 questions (not "answers" this time) based on the same chapter used in the previous two tasks. Again, you must find NEW information that you have not yet used. Now it's getting hard to find that new information! Again, give your questions to a friend to answer.

Step 6

As you have been doing the puzzles, your brain has been actively searching for new information. Now write a NEW LIST that contains only the new information you have discovered when doing the puzzles. Your new list is the one to look at repeatedly for short bursts over the next few days. Try to remember more and more of it without looking at it. After a few days, you should be able to add words from your second list to your first list as you increase the information in your long-term memory.

FINALLY! Be inspired...

Make a list of different revision ideas and beside each one write **THINGS I HAVE** tried, **THINGS I WILL** try and **THINGS I MIGHT** try. Don't be scared of trying something new.

And remember – "FAIL TO PREPARE AND PREPARE TO FAIL!"

Higher Physics

The course

In Higher Physics you will learn more about how the world around you works as you study areas such as kinematics, forces, energy, electricity, electronics, semiconductors, waves, light and radioactivity. As a result of following the Higher Physics course, you should acquire:

- an increased knowledge and understanding of facts and ideas, of techniques and of the applications of physics in society
- skills in applying your knowledge and understanding in a wide variety of theoretical and practical problem solving contexts
- skills associated with carrying out experimental and investigative work in physics and analysing the information obtained.

How the course is graded

The marks that you achieve in the final examination determine your grade for Higher Physics. That is why it is so important that you prepare properly for the exam – this book is all about helping you to do that! However, in order to receive a course award, you must also be successful in both of the following (internally marked by your teacher):

- **the unit tests (or NABs)**

  You must *pass* one test for each of the three units (Mechanics and the Properties of Matter; Electricity and Electronics; Radiation and Matter). Each unit assessment (or test) lasts for 45 minutes and consists of a total of 30 marks. The pass mark is 18 marks. More than one attempt to pass a unit assessment is permitted.

- **practical assessment**

  During the course, you must have been actively involved in at least one experiment and have completed a write-up for it. You must successfully complete one experimental write-up to the standards laid down by the SQA.

The exam

The exam lasts 2 hours 30 minutes and contains two sections:

- Section A has 20 marks for 20 multiple choice questions.
- Section B has 70 marks for extended answer questions.

All questions should be attempted. The marks are evenly divided across the units in the course – i.e. there are around 30 marks for each of the three units. Approximately 40% of the total 90 marks are classified as Knowledge and Understanding (K&U) and 60% Problem Solving (PS).

To achieve an award at 'A' or 'B', you need to gain most of the marks for Knowledge and Understanding and also a high proportion of the Problem Solving marks.

Knowledge and Understanding questions are about being able to recall facts, symbols, diagrams, ideas and techniques. Being able to use relationships (formulas) to carry out straightforward calculations is also part of Knowledge and Understanding.

Problem Solving is about being able to apply your knowledge and understanding so that you can answer questions which are presented in a way or context slightly different to what you are likely to have met. Approximately half of the Problem Solving marks in the final examination are for questions of a 'more complex nature' which may be set in a more complicated context or be presented in a less structured way.

The SQA provides detailed information about the Higher Physics Course and its assessment on the following page of its website: http://www.sqa.org.uk/sqa/47916/html.

Tips for success

The following advice is designed to help improve your success in the Higher Physics examination. It is based on analysis of the performance of candidates in recent national examinations and the SQA's consequent recommendations.

Before the examination

Ensure you know your notes and textbook very well. This requires regular reading and re-reading of your notes and attempting to write out facts, symbols, diagrams and such like from memory.

In addition to this, get to know the Content Statements for the course very well (these are also available on the SQA's website.

Make sure you are fully familiar with all the information provided in the data sheet on page two of the examination paper and that you have learned the symbols and units for each of the quantities listed in the Physics data booklet. It is important to learn to use all of the relationships in the Physics data booklet as well as the mathematical formulae and periodic table near the back.

Be aware that you may need to state or derive other relationships which are not listed in the Physics data booklet; for example, the component of weight of an object down a slope.

Practise answering numerical questions on a regular basis to ensure that you are very familiar with using all the formulae in the course. Compare your attempts with the official answers and improve any identified weaknesses.

Practise presenting your final answers to numerical calculations to an appropriate number of significant figures. This should be the same as the number of significant figures given in the provided data. For example, the mass of an electron is given on the data sheet as 9.11×10^{-31} kg – this value is to three significant figures.

Practise rounding off figures correctly too. For example a figure of '26.57' rounded to three significant figures should be '26.6', not '26.5'.

Practising answering non-calculator past paper questions, especially those which require you to 'describe', 'explain' or 'justify', is also a very important part of your preparation for the final examination. You can compare your answers with the official ones. Perhaps your teacher might be able to help by marking your attempts and giving advice.

Be sure to spend time learning correct technical terminology (for example, total internal reflection occurs whenever the incident angle is *greater than* the critical angle; op-amps saturate, not voltages). Spend time learning correct spelling (like fusion, not *fussion*) too!

Make sure you know all the prefixes required for the course and practise using the correct power of ten for each prefix (e.g '420 nF' means '420 nanofarads' and equals 420×10^{-9} F). Note that these prefixes are not provided in the data booklet and so must be memorised.

Practise presenting your answers on blank paper if you can. Make sure you can present written paragraphs, clearly structured calculations and neat diagrams on unlined paper prior to sitting the examination.

Make sure you are clear about the difference between absolute and percentage uncertainties. You should practise converting from one to the other.

During the examination

On the day of the examination, read each question very carefully and ensure that your response really does answer what has been asked. Re-reading the question immediately after writing your answer can be a useful way to check! This way, you will reduce the chance of giving an inappropriate or incomplete answer. You should use the number of marks allocated to each part of a question as a guide to the extent of calculation or explanation required. For example, it is very unlikely that a question which has been allocated three marks can be answered fully by a single calculation using only one formula.

Take great care to label each answer to match the correct part of a question. A wrongly labelled answer can result in no marks being awarded. Write your answers as legibly as you can! If you wish to change an answer, it is usually better to rewrite the answer than to 'overwrite' the original answer. If you make two (or more) attempts for the same part of a question, you must score through the part(s) that you do not wish to be considered by the marker – you must not leave alternative answers.

Present your numerical analyses in a clear and structured way – markers need to be able to follow the logic in your answers. This may require you to re-write an answer after doing some rough working. Take great care to transfer data accurately from the question paper to your answer, otherwise you will lose most of the marks. For example, making the mistake of writing Planck's constant as 6.36×10^{-34} instead of 6.63×10^{-34} is easily avoided if you carefully check the information you have transferred.

In numerical calculations, be sure to round off values only at the final answer for a part of a question. The answer(s) to any intermediate calculation(s) should not be rounded as this could cause inaccuracy in the final answer.

Be careful to take into account the vector nature of **u**, **v** and **a** in the equations of motion and other relationships such as change in momentum ($= mv - mu$) and ensure that you substitute their values as being positive or negative as appropriate. Remember to quote a direction as well as a magnitude when giving vector quantities as answers.

Take care to make sure that any diagrams you draw are accurate, neat and complete. For example, in a vector diagram, draw each line with a ruler, making sure that it is exactly the correct length to your chosen scale and that an arrow is added to show its direction. Carefully use a protractor to ensure that angles are precisely drawn and clearly mark the values of any important angles. Try to use a ruler when drawing any straight lines, especially when drawing the axes of graphs and the paths taken by rays of light.

Understand that to 'sketch' a graph does not mean that the graph can be untidy or inaccurate. The instruction to 'sketch' a graph only means that it does not have to be drawn to scale. Care should still be taken to present your sketch as neatly as possible. For example, a ruler should be used to draw the axes and any straight sections of the graph line. The origin and axes on sketch graphs must also be labelled and any important values carefully shown. It is useful to link these important values to the relevant parts of the graph line using dotted reference lines. It is wise to use a pencil when attempting to draw the graph line – any wrong line(s) can then be erased to leave a neat, clear, single line as the final answer.

Do not use up ($\uparrow$) and down ($\downarrow$) arrows in your answers – instead, use words such as 'increases' and 'decreases'. Arrows are fine in your own notes, but you should not use them when attempting to communicate Physics to others – particularly in examination answers!

Start your answer to any 'show' question by quoting an appropriate formula before using any numbers/values. The substitution of numbers should then use the data given in the question without any 'mental arithmetic' having been performed. Then work out a final answer which matches what you were asked to show.

Be aware that in a must justify question, no marks can be awarded if you make no attempt at a justification. So, make an attempt! Try to identify the relevant Physics for the given situation (perhaps a formula) and describe how changing one factor affects the other(s).

Good luck!

Remember that the rewards for passing Higher Physics are well worth it! Your pass will help you get the future you want for yourself. In the exam, be confident in your own ability. If you're not sure how to answer a question, trust your instincts and just give it a go anyway – keep calm and don't panic! GOOD LUCK!

HIGHER

2009

[BLANK PAGE]

X069/301

NATIONAL QUALIFICATIONS 2009	TUESDAY, 26 MAY 1.00 PM – 3.30 PM	PHYSICS HIGHER

Read Carefully

Reference may be made to the Physics Data Booklet.

1 All questions should be attempted.

Section A (questions 1 to 20)

2 Check that the answer sheet is for Physics Higher (Section A).

3 For this section of the examination you must use an **HB pencil** and, where necessary, an eraser.

4 Check that the answer sheet you have been given has **your name**, **date of birth**, **SCN** (Scottish Candidate Number) and **Centre Name** printed on it.
   Do not change any of these details.

5 If any of this information is wrong, tell the Invigilator immediately.

6 If this information is correct, **print** your name and seat number in the boxes provided.

7 There is **only one correct** answer to each question.

8 Any rough working should be done on the question paper or the rough working sheet, **not** on your answer sheet.

9 At the end of the exam, put the **answer sheet for Section A inside the front cover of your answer book**.

10 Instructions as to how to record your answers to questions 1–20 are given on page three.

Section B (questions 21 to 30)

11 Answer the questions numbered 21 to 30 in the answer book provided.

12 **All answers must be written clearly and legibly in ink**.

13 Fill in the details on the front of the answer book.

14 Enter the question number clearly in the margin of the answer book beside each of your answers to questions 21 to 30.

15 Care should be taken to give an appropriate number of significant figures in the final answers to calculations.

16 Where additional paper, eg square ruled paper, is used, write your name and SCN (Scottish Candidate Number) on it and place it inside the front cover of your answer booklet.

DATA SHEET
COMMON PHYSICAL QUANTITIES

Quantity	Symbol	Value	Quantity	Symbol	Value
Speed of light in vacuum	c	$3 \cdot 00 \times 10^8 \, \text{m s}^{-1}$	Mass of electron	m_e	$9 \cdot 11 \times 10^{-31} \, \text{kg}$
Magnitude of the charge on an electron	e	$1 \cdot 60 \times 10^{-19} \, \text{C}$	Mass of neutron	m_n	$1 \cdot 675 \times 10^{-27} \, \text{kg}$
Gravitational acceleration on Earth	g	$9 \cdot 8 \, \text{m s}^{-2}$	Mass of proton	m_p	$1 \cdot 673 \times 10^{-27} \, \text{kg}$
Planck's constant	h	$6 \cdot 63 \times 10^{-34} \, \text{J s}$			

REFRACTIVE INDICES

The refractive indices refer to sodium light of wavelength 589 nm and to substances at a temperature of 273 K.

Substance	Refractive index	Substance	Refractive index
Diamond	2·42	Water	1·33
Crown glass	1·50	Air	1·00

SPECTRAL LINES

Element	Wavelength/nm	Colour	Element	Wavelength/nm	Colour
Hydrogen	656	Red	Cadmium	644	Red
	486	Blue-green		509	Green
	434	Blue-violet		480	Blue
	410	Violet	*Lasers*		
	397	Ultraviolet	Element	Wavelength/nm	Colour
	389	Ultraviolet	Carbon dioxide	9550 } 10590	Infrared
Sodium	589	Yellow	Helium-neon	633	Red

PROPERTIES OF SELECTED MATERIALS

Substance	Density/ kg m^{-3}	Melting Point/ K	Boiling Point/ K
Aluminium	$2 \cdot 70 \times 10^3$	933	2623
Copper	$8 \cdot 96 \times 10^3$	1357	2853
Ice	$9 \cdot 20 \times 10^2$	273	. . . .
Sea Water	$1 \cdot 02 \times 10^3$	264	377
Water	$1 \cdot 00 \times 10^3$	273	373
Air	1·29	. . . .	. . . .
Hydrogen	$9 \cdot 0 \times 10^{-2}$	14	20

The gas densities refer to a temperature of 273 K and a pressure of $1 \cdot 01 \times 10^5$ Pa.

SECTION A

For questions 1 to 20 in this section of the paper the answer to each question is either A, B, C, D or E. Decide what your answer is, then, using your pencil, put a horizontal line in the space provided—see the example below.

EXAMPLE

The energy unit measured by the electricity meter in your home is the

    A kilowatt-hour

    B ampere

    C watt

    D coulomb

    E volt.

The correct answer is **A**—kilowatt-hour. The answer **A** has been clearly marked in **pencil** with a horizontal line (see below).

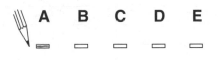

Changing an answer

If you decide to change your answer, carefully erase your first answer and, using your pencil, fill in the answer you want. The answer below has been changed to **E**.

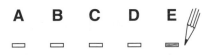

[Turn over

SECTION A

Answer questions 1–20 on the answer sheet.

1. Which of the following contains one vector and one scalar quantity?

   A   power; speed

   B   force; kinetic energy

   C   momentum; velocity

   D   work; potential energy

   E   displacement; acceleration

2. The following velocity-time graph represents the vertical motion of a ball.

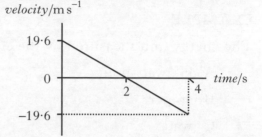

   Which of the following acceleration-time graphs represents the same motion?

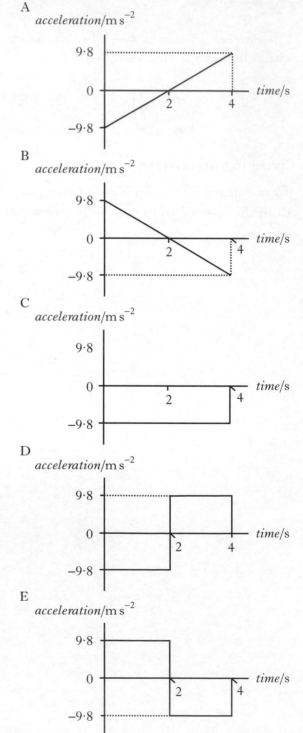

3. A box of weight 120 N is placed on a smooth horizontal surface.
A force of 20 N is applied to the box as shown.

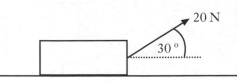

The box is pulled a distance of 50 m along the surface.

The work done in pulling the box is

A   500 J

B   866 J

C   1000 J

D   6000 J

E   6866 J.

4. A skydiver of total mass 85 kg is falling vertically.

At one point during the fall, the air resistance on the skydiver is 135 N.

The acceleration of the skydiver at this point is

A $0.6\,\mathrm{m\,s^{-2}}$

B $1.6\,\mathrm{m\,s^{-2}}$

C $6.2\,\mathrm{m\,s^{-2}}$

D $8.2\,\mathrm{m\,s^{-2}}$

E $13.8\,\mathrm{m\,s^{-2}}$.

5. A 2·0 kg trolley travels in a straight line towards a stationary 5·0 kg trolley as shown.

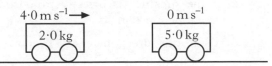

The trolleys collide. After the collision the trolleys move as shown below.

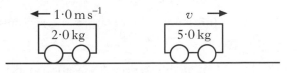

What is the speed v of the 5·0 kg trolley after the collision?

A $0.4\,\mathrm{m\,s^{-1}}$

B $1.2\,\mathrm{m\,s^{-1}}$

C $2.0\,\mathrm{m\,s^{-1}}$

D $2.2\,\mathrm{m\,s^{-1}}$

E $3.0\,\mathrm{m\,s^{-1}}$

6. The density of the gas in a container is initially $5.0\,\mathrm{kg\,m^{-3}}$.

Which of the following increases the density of the gas?

I Raising the temperature of the gas without changing its mass or volume.

II Increasing the mass of the gas without changing its volume or temperature.

III Increasing the volume of the gas without changing its mass or temperature.

A   II only

B   III only

C   I and II only

D   II and III only

E   I, II and III

[Turn over

7. For a fixed mass of gas at constant volume

A the pressure is directly proportional to temperature in °C

B the pressure is inversely proportional to temperature in °C

C the pressure is directly proportional to temperature in K

D the pressure is inversely proportional to temperature in K

E (pressure × temperature in K) is constant.

8. A potential difference, V, is applied between two metal plates. The plates are 0·15 m apart. A charge of +4·0 mC is released from rest at the positively charged plate as shown.

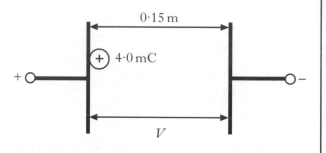

The kinetic energy of the charge just before it hits the negative plate is 8·0 J.

The potential difference between the plates is

A $3·2 \times 10^{-2}$ V

B 1·2 V

C 2·0 V

D $2·0 \times 10^3$ V

E $4·0 \times 10^3$ V.

9. A battery of e.m.f. 24 V and negligible internal resistance is connected as shown.

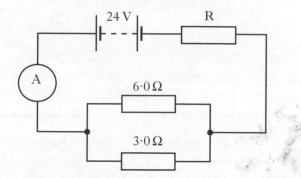

The reading on the ammeter is 2·0 A.

The resistance of R is

A 3·0 Ω

B 4·0 Ω

C 10 Ω

D 12 Ω

E 18 Ω.

10. The diagram shows a Wheatstone Bridge.

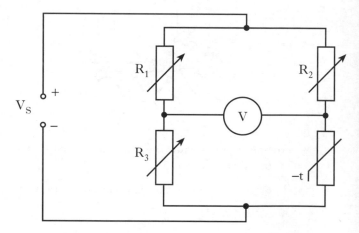

The bridge is initially balanced.

The thermistor is then heated and its resistance decreases. The bridge could be returned to balance by

A decreasing R_1

B decreasing R_2

C increasing R_2

D increasing R_3

E increasing V_S.

11. A $25 \cdot 0\,\mu\text{F}$ capacitor is charged until the potential difference across it is $500\,\text{V}$.

The charge stored in the capacitor is

A $5 \cdot 00 \times 10^{-8}\,\text{C}$

B $2 \cdot 00 \times 10^{-5}\,\text{C}$

C $1 \cdot 25 \times 10^{-2}\,\text{C}$

D $1 \cdot 25 \times 10^{4}\,\text{C}$

E $2 \cdot 00 \times 10^{7}\,\text{C}$.

12. A student connects an a.c. supply to an a.c. ammeter and a component **X**.

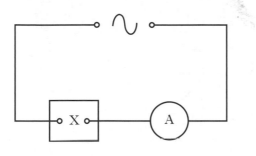

As the frequency of the a.c. supply is steadily increased, the ammeter reading also increases.

Component **X** is a

A   capacitor

B   diode

C   lamp

D   resistor

E   transistor.

13. An amplifier circuit is set up as shown.

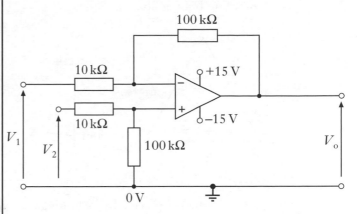

When $V_\text{o} = 0 \cdot 60\,\text{V}$ and $V_1 = 2 \cdot 70\,\text{V}$, what is the value of V_2?

A $2 \cdot 10\,\text{V}$

B $2 \cdot 64\,\text{V}$

C $2 \cdot 76\,\text{V}$

D $3 \cdot 30\,\text{V}$

E $8 \cdot 70\,\text{V}$

[Turn over

14. A prism is used to produce a spectrum from a source of white light as shown.

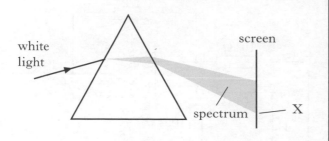

The colour observed at X is noted.

The prism is then replaced by a grating to produce spectra as shown.

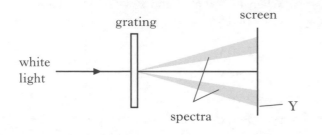

The colour observed at Y is noted.

Which row in the table gives the colour and wavelength of the light observed at X and the light observed at Y?

	Colour of light at X	Wavelength of light at X/nm	Colour of light at Y	Wavelength of light at Y/nm
A	Red	450	Red	450
B	Blue	450	Blue	450
C	Blue	650	Red	450
D	Blue	450	Red	650
E	Red	650	Blue	450

15. A ray of monochromatic light passes into a glass block as shown.

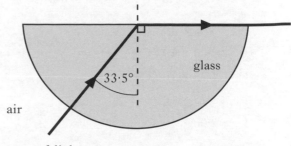

The refractive index of the glass for this light is

A 0·03

B 0·55

C 0·87

D 1·20

E 1·81.

16. Which of the following statements about the characteristics of laser light is/are true?

   I It is monochromatic since all the photons have the same frequency.

   II It is coherent because all the photons are in phase.

   III Its irradiance is inversely proportional to the square of the distance from the source.

A I only

B I and II only

C I and III only

D II and III only

E I, II and III

17. A student writes the following statements about p-type semiconductor material.

    I   Most charge carriers are positive.

    II The p-type material has a positive charge.

    III Impurity atoms in the material have 3 outer electrons.

    Which of these statements is/are true?

    A   I only

    B   II only

    C   I and II only

    D   I and III only

    E   I, II and III

18. A p-n junction diode is forward biased.

    Positive and negative charge carriers recombine in the junction region. This causes the emission of

    A   a hole

    B   an electron

    C   an electron-hole pair

    D   a proton

    E   a photon.

19. A sample of radioactive material has a mass of 20 g. There are 48 000 nuclear decays every minute in this sample.

    The activity of the sample is

    A   800 Bq

    B   2400 Bq

    C   48 000 Bq

    D   2 400 000 Bq

    E   2 880 000 Bq.

20. A sample of body tissue is irradiated by two different types of radiation, X and Y.

    The table gives the radiation weighting factor and absorbed dose for each radiation.

Type of radiation	Radiation weighting factor	Absorbed dose/μGy
X	10	5
Y	5	2

    The total equivalent dose received by the tissue is

    A $0 \cdot 9\,\mu$Sv

    B $4 \cdot 5\,\mu$Sv

    C $7 \cdot 0\,\mu$Sv

    D $40 \cdot 0\,\mu$Sv

    E $60 \cdot 0\,\mu$Sv.

[Turn over

SECTION B

Write your answers to questions 21 to 30 in the answer book.

Marks

21. A basketball player throws a ball with an initial velocity of $6.5 \, \text{m s}^{-1}$ at an angle of $50°$ to the horizontal. The ball is $2.3 \, \text{m}$ above the ground when released.

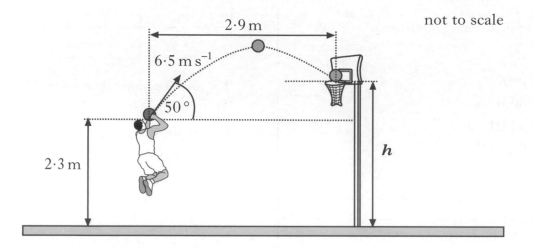

The ball travels a horizontal distance of $2.9 \, \text{m}$ to reach the top of the basket. The effects of air resistance can be ignored.

(a) Calculate:

   (i) the horizontal component of the initial velocity of the ball;   **1**

   (ii) the vertical component of the initial velocity of the ball.   **1**

(b) Show that the time taken for the ball to reach the basket is $0.69 \, \text{s}$.   **1**

(c) Calculate the height **h** of the top of the basket.   **2**

(d) A student observing the player makes the following statement.

"The player should throw the ball with a higher speed at the same angle. The ball would then land in the basket as before but it would take a shorter time to travel the 2·9 metres."

Explain why the student's statement is incorrect.   **2**

                                              (7)

Marks

22. Golf clubs are tested to ensure they meet certain standards.

(a) In one test, a securely held clubhead is hit by a small steel pendulum. The time of contact between the clubhead and the pendulum is recorded.

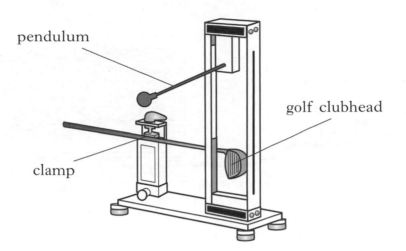

The experiment is repeated several times.

The results are shown.

    248 μs   259 μs   251 μs   263 μs   254 μs

   (i)   Calculate:

       (A)   the mean contact time between the clubhead and the pendulum;   **1**

       (B)   the approximate absolute random uncertainty in this value.   **1**

  (ii)   In this test, the standard required is that the maximum value of the mean contact time must not be greater than 257 μs.

       Does the club meet this standard?

       You must justify your answer.   **1**

(b) In another test, a machine uses a club to hit a stationary golf ball.

The mass of the ball is $4 \cdot 5 \times 10^{-2}$ kg. The ball leaves the club with a speed of $50 \cdot 0 \, \text{m s}^{-1}$. The time of contact between the club and ball is 450 μs.

   (i)   Calculate the average force exerted on the ball by the club.   **2**

  (ii)   The test is repeated using a different club and an identical ball. The machine applies the same average force on the ball but with a longer contact time.

       What effect, if any, does this have on the speed of the ball as it leaves the club?

       Justify your answer.   **2**

                                                            (7)

Marks

23. A student is training to become a diver.

(*a*) The student carries out an experiment to investigate the relationship between the pressure and volume of a fixed mass of gas using the apparatus shown.

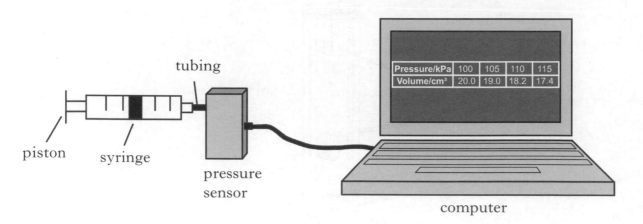

The pressure of the gas is recorded using a pressure sensor connected to a computer. The volume of the gas is also recorded. The student pushes the piston to alter the volume and a series of readings is taken.
The temperature of the gas is constant during the experiment.

The results are shown.

Pressure/kPa	100	105	110	115
Volume/cm^3	20·0	19·0	18·2	17·4

  (i) Using **all** the data, establish the relationship between the pressure and volume of the gas.   2

  (ii) Use the kinetic model to explain the change in pressure as the volume of gas decreases.   2

(*b*) (i) The density of water in a loch is $1·02 \times 10^3 \, \text{kg m}^{-3}$. Atmospheric pressure is $1·01 \times 10^5 \, \text{Pa}$.

  Show that the **total** pressure at a depth of 12·0 m in this loch is $2·21 \times 10^5 \, \text{Pa}$.   2

  (ii) At the surface of the loch, the student breathes in a volume of $1·50 \times 10^{-3} \, \text{m}^3$ of air.

  Calculate the volume this air would occupy at a depth of 12·0 m. The mass and temperature of the air are constant.   2

(*c*) At a depth of 12·0 m, the diver fills her lungs with air from her breathing apparatus. She then swims to the surface.

  Explain why it would be dangerous for her to hold her breath while doing this.   2

                                                                                                                                                                    (10)

Marks

24. A battery of e.m.f. 6·0 V and internal resistance, *r*, is connected to a variable resistor R as shown.

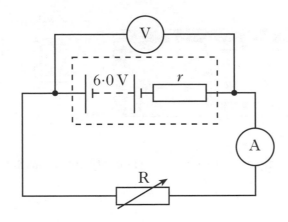

The graph shows how the current in the circuit changes as the resistance of R increases.

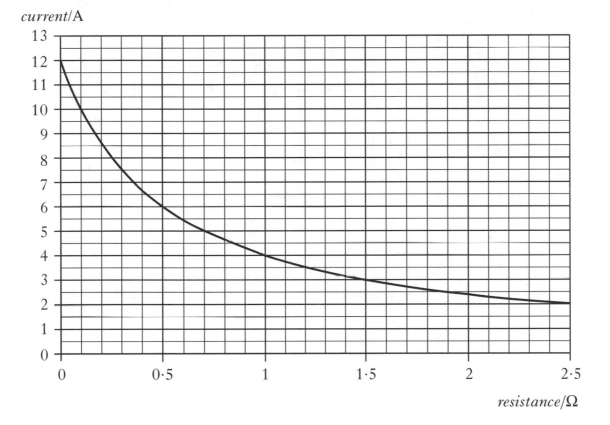

(a) Use information from the graph to calculate:

   (i)   the lost volts in the circuit when the resistance of R is 1·5 Ω;   2

   (ii) the internal resistance, *r*, of the battery.   2

(b) The resistance of R is now increased.

   What effect, if any, does this have on the lost volts?

   You must justify your answer.   2

   (6)

Marks

25.   (a) A microphone is connected to the input terminals of an oscilloscope.
          A tuning fork is made to vibrate and held close to the microphone as shown.

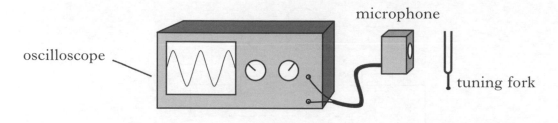

The following diagram shows the trace obtained and the settings on the oscilloscope.

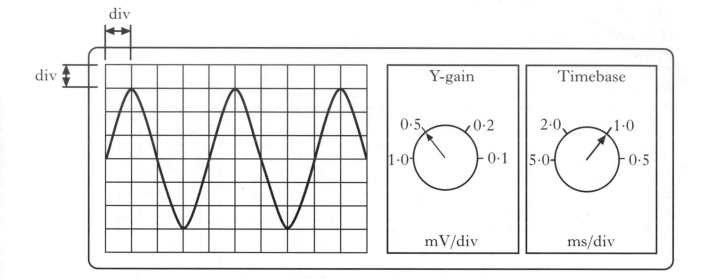

Calculate:

(i)   the peak voltage of the signal;   1

(ii) the frequency of the signal.   2

Marks

25. (continued)

(b) To amplify the signal from the microphone, it is connected to an op-amp circuit. The oscilloscope is now connected to the output of the amplifier as shown.

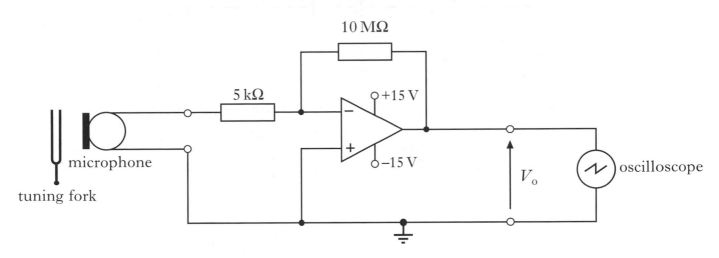

The settings of the oscilloscope are adjusted to show a trace of the amplified signal.

(i) In which mode is this op amp being used?   1

(ii) The peak voltage from the microphone is now 6·2 mV.

Calculate the **r.m.s.** value of the output voltage, V_o, of the op-amp.   3

(iii) With the same input signal and settings on the oscilloscope, the supply voltage to the op-amp is now reduced from ± 15 V to ± 9 V.

What effect does this change have on the trace on the oscilloscope?

Justify your answer.   2

    (9)

[Turn over

Marks

26. A 12 volt battery of negligible internal resistance is connected in a circuit as shown.

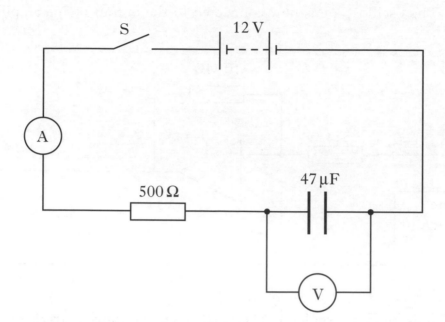

The capacitor is initially uncharged. Switch S is then closed and the capacitor starts to charge.

(a) Sketch a graph of the current against time from the instant switch S is closed. Numerical values are not required.   1

(b) At one instant during the charging of the capacitor the reading on the ammeter is 5·0 mA.

Calculate the reading on the voltmeter at this instant.   3

(c) Calculate the **maximum** energy stored in the capacitor in this circuit.   2

(d) The 500 Ω resistor is now replaced with a 2·0 kΩ resistor.

What effect, if any, does this have on the maximum energy stored in the capacitor?

Justify your answer.   2

    (8)

Marks

27. A laser produces a narrow beam of monochromatic light.

(a) Red light from a laser passes through a grating as shown.

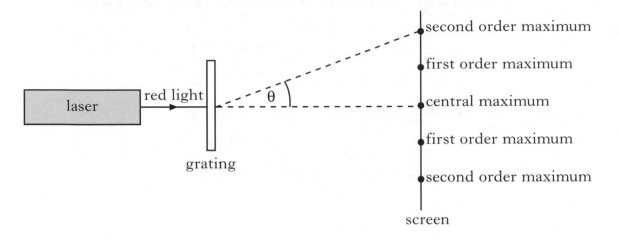

A series of maxima and minima is observed.

Explain in terms of waves how a **minimum** is produced.

1

(b) The laser is now replaced by a second laser, which emits blue light.

Explain why the observed maxima are now closer together.

1

(c) The wavelength of the blue light from the second laser is 4.73×10^{-7} m. The spacing between the lines on the grating is 2.00×10^{-6} m.

Calculate the angle between the central maximum and the second order maximum.

2

(4)

[Turn over

Marks

28. (*a*) Electrons which orbit the nucleus of an atom can be considered as occupying discrete energy levels.

The following diagram shows some of the energy levels for a particular atom.

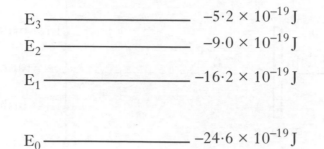

$$E_3 \quad\text{————————}\quad -5 \cdot 2 \times 10^{-19}\,J$$
$$E_2 \quad\text{————————}\quad -9 \cdot 0 \times 10^{-19}\,J$$
$$E_1 \quad\text{————————}\quad -16 \cdot 2 \times 10^{-19}\,J$$
$$E_0 \quad\text{————————}\quad -24 \cdot 6 \times 10^{-19}\,J$$

(i) Radiation is produced when electrons make transitions from a higher to a lower energy level.

Which transition, between these energy levels, produces radiation with the shortest wavelength?

Justify your answer. 2

(ii) An electron is excited from energy level E_2 to E_3 by absorbing light energy.

What frequency of light is used to excite this electron? 2

(*b*) Another source of light has a frequency of $4 \cdot 6 \times 10^{14}\,Hz$ in air.

A ray of this light is directed into a block of transparent material as shown.

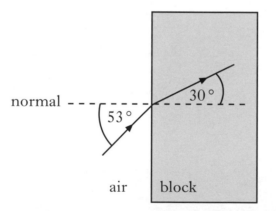

normal

53°

30°

air   block

Calculate the wavelength of the light in the block. 3

(7)

Marks

29. Ultraviolet radiation from a lamp is incident on the surface of a metal.

This causes the release of electrons from the surface of the metal.

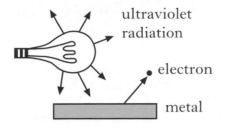

The energy of each photon of ultraviolet light is $5 \cdot 23 \times 10^{-19}$ J.

The work function of the metal is $2 \cdot 56 \times 10^{-19}$ J.

(a) Calculate:

    (i) the maximum kinetic energy of an electron released from this metal by this radiation;   1

    (ii) the maximum speed of an emitted electron.   2

(b) The source of ultraviolet radiation is now moved further away from the surface of the metal.

State the effect, if any, this has on the maximum speed of an emitted electron.

Justify your answer.   2

   (5)

[Turn over

Marks

30. (*a*) Some power stations use nuclear fission reactions to provide energy for generating electricity. The following statement represents a fission reaction.

$$^{235}_{92}U \ + \ ^{1}_{0}n \ \rightarrow \ ^{139}_{57}La \ + \ ^{r}_{42}Mo \ + \ 2\,^{1}_{0}n \ + \ s\,^{0}_{-1}e$$

(i) Determine the numbers represented by the letters *r* and *s* in the above statement.   **1**

(ii) Explain why a nuclear fission reaction releases energy.   **1**

(iii) The masses of the particles involved in the reaction are shown in the table.

Particle	Mass/kg
$^{235}_{92}U$	$390 \cdot 173 \times 10^{-27}$
$^{139}_{57}La$	$230 \cdot 584 \times 10^{-27}$
$^{r}_{42}Mo$	$157 \cdot 544 \times 10^{-27}$
$^{1}_{0}n$	$1 \cdot 675 \times 10^{-27}$
$^{0}_{-1}e$	negligible

Calculate the energy released in this reaction.   **3**

Marks

30. (continued)

(b) One method of reducing the radiation received by a person is by using lead shielding.

In an investigation of the absorption of gamma radiation by lead, the following graph of corrected count rate against thickness of lead is obtained.

corrected count rate/counts per minute

(i) Determine the half-value thickness of lead for this radiation. 1

(ii) With no shielding, the equivalent dose rate a short distance from this source is $200\,\mu Sv\,h^{-1}$.

When the source is stored in a lead container, the equivalent dose rate at the same distance falls to $50\,\mu Sv\,h^{-1}$.

Calculate the thickness of the lead container. 1

(7)

[END OF QUESTION PAPER]

[BLANK PAGE]

[BLANK PAGE]

X069/301

NATIONAL
QUALIFICATIONS
2010

FRIDAY, 28 MAY
1.00 PM – 3.30 PM

PHYSICS
HIGHER

Read Carefully

Reference may be made to the Physics Data Booklet.

1 All questions should be attempted.

Section A (questions 1 to 20)

2 Check that the answer sheet is for Physics Higher (Section A).

3 For this section of the examination you must use an **HB pencil** and, where necessary, an eraser.

4 Check that the answer sheet you have been given has **your name**, **date of birth**, **SCN** (Scottish Candidate Number) and **Centre Name** printed on it.

   Do not change any of these details.

5 If any of this information is wrong, tell the Invigilator immediately.

6 If this information is correct, **print** your name and seat number in the boxes provided.

7 There is **only one correct** answer to each question.

8 Any rough working should be done on the question paper or the rough working sheet, **not** on your answer sheet.

9 At the end of the exam, put the **answer sheet for Section A inside the front cover of your answer book**.

10 Instructions as to how to record your answers to questions 1–20 are given on page three.

Section B (questions 21 to 30)

11 Answer the questions numbered 21 to 30 in the answer book provided.

12 **All answers must be written clearly and legibly in ink**.

13 Fill in the details on the front of the answer book.

14 Enter the question number clearly in the margin of the answer book beside each of your answers to questions 21 to 30.

15 Care should be taken to give an appropriate number of significant figures in the final answers to calculations.

16 Where additional paper, eg square ruled paper, is used, write your name and SCN (Scottish Candidate Number) on it and place it inside the front cover of your answer booklet.

DATA SHEET
COMMON PHYSICAL QUANTITIES

Quantity	Symbol	Value	Quantity	Symbol	Value
Speed of light in vacuum	c	3.00×10^8 m s^{-1}	Mass of electron	m_e	9.11×10^{-31} kg
Magnitude of the charge on an electron	e	1.60×10^{-19} C	Mass of neutron	m_n	1.675×10^{-27} kg
Gravitational acceleration on Earth	g	9.8 m s^{-2}	Mass of proton	m_p	1.673×10^{-27} kg
Planck's constant	h	6.63×10^{-34} J s			

REFRACTIVE INDICES
The refractive indices refer to sodium light of wavelength 589 nm and to substances at a temperature of 273 K.

Substance	Refractive index	Substance	Refractive index
Diamond	2·42	Water	1·33
Crown glass	1·50	Air	1·00

SPECTRAL LINES

Element	Wavelength/nm	Colour	Element	Wavelength/nm	Colour
Hydrogen	656	Red	Cadmium	644	Red
	486	Blue-green		509	Green
	434	Blue-violet		480	Blue
	410	Violet			
	397	Ultraviolet		Lasers	
	389	Ultraviolet	Element	Wavelength/nm	Colour
			Carbon dioxide	9550 } 10590	Infrared
Sodium	589	Yellow	Helium-neon	633	Red

PROPERTIES OF SELECTED MATERIALS

Substance	Density/ kg m^{-3}	Melting Point/ K	Boiling Point/ K
Aluminium	2.70×10^3	933	2623
Copper	8.96×10^3	1357	2853
Ice	9.20×10^2	273	. . . .
Sea Water	1.02×10^3	264	377
Water	1.00×10^3	273	373
Air	1·29	. . . .	. . . .
Hydrogen	9.0×10^{-2}	14	20

The gas densities refer to a temperature of 273 K and a pressure of 1.01×10^5 Pa.

SECTION A

For questions 1 to 20 in this section of the paper the answer to each question is either A, B, C, D or E. Decide what your answer is, then, using your pencil, put a horizontal line in the space provided—see the example below.

EXAMPLE

The energy unit measured by the electricity meter in your home is the

    A kilowatt-hour

    B ampere

    C watt

    D coulomb

    E volt.

The correct answer is **A**—kilowatt-hour. The answer **A** has been clearly marked in **pencil** with a horizontal line (see below).

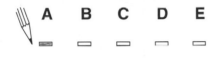

Changing an answer

If you decide to change your answer, carefully erase your first answer and, using your pencil, fill in the answer you want. The answer below has been changed to **E**.

[Turn over

SECTION A

Answer questions 1–20 on the answer sheet.

1. Acceleration is the change in

    A distance per unit time

    B displacement per unit time

    C velocity per unit distance

    D speed per unit time

    E velocity per unit time.

2. The graph shows how the acceleration, a, of an object varies with time, t.

    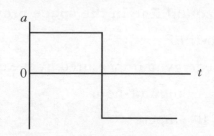

    Which graph shows how the velocity, v, of the object varies with time, t?

    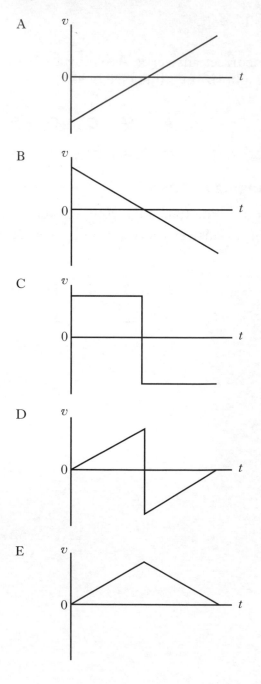

3. A car of mass 1000 kg is travelling at a speed of 40 m s^{-1} along a race track. The brakes are applied and the speed of the car decreases to 10 m s^{-1}.

   How much kinetic energy is lost by the car?

   A   15 kJ

   B   50 kJ

   C   450 kJ

   D   750 kJ

   E   800 kJ

4. A substance can exist as a solid, a liquid or a gas.

   Which row in the table shows the approximate relative magnitudes of the densities of the substance in these states?

	Density of solid	Density of liquid	Density of gas
A	1000	1000	1
B	10	10	1000
C	1	1	1000
D	1000	10	1
E	1	1	10

5. A fish is swimming at a depth of 10·4 m.

   The density of the water is $1·03 \times 10^3$ kg m^{-3}.

   The pressure at this depth caused by the water is

   A $0·99 \times 10^2$ Pa

   B $1·04 \times 10^4$ Pa

   C $1·07 \times 10^4$ Pa

   D $1·05 \times 10^5$ Pa

   E $1·07 \times 10^5$ Pa.

6. Ice at a temperature of –10 °C is heated until it becomes water at 80 °C.

   The temperature change in kelvin is

   A   70 K

   B   90 K

   C   343 K

   D   363 K

   E   636 K.

7. The potential difference between two points is

   A   the work done in moving one electron between the two points

   B   the voltage between the two points when there is a current of one ampere

   C   the work done in moving one coulomb of charge between the two points

   D   the kinetic energy gained by an electron as it moves between the two points

   E   the work done in moving any charge between the two points.

8. The product, X, of a nuclear reaction passes through an electric field as shown.

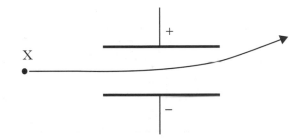

   Product X is

   A   an alpha particle

   B   a beta particle

   C   gamma radiation

   D   a fast neutron

   E   a slow neutron.

[Turn over

9. Which of the following combinations of resistors has the greatest resistance between X and Y?

A
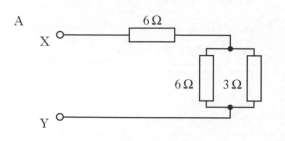

B
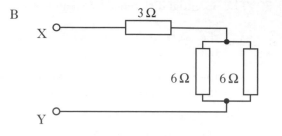

C
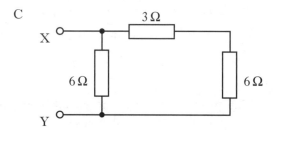

D
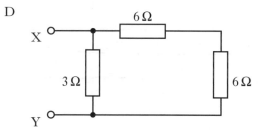

E
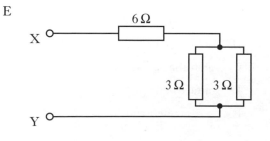

10. In the following Wheatstone bridge circuit, the reading on the voltmeter is zero when the resistance of R is set at 1 kΩ.

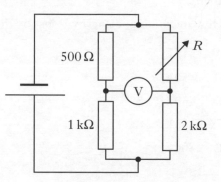

Which of the following is the graph of the voltmeter reading V against the resistance R?

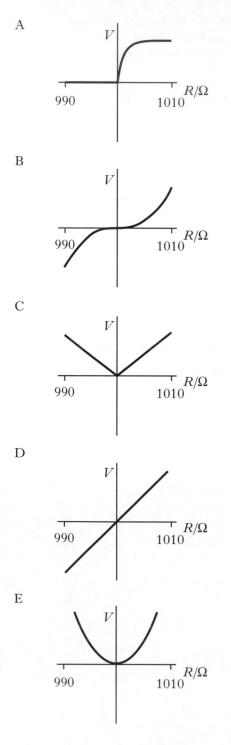

11. A student makes the following statements about capacitors.

    I   Capacitors block a.c. signals.

    II   Capacitors store energy.

    III Capacitors store charge.

Which of these statements is/are true?

  A   I only

  B   I and II only

  C   I and III only

  D   II and III only

  E   I, II and III

12. A circuit is set up as shown.

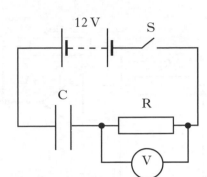

The capacitor is initially uncharged. Switch S is now closed. Which graph shows how the potential difference, V, across R, varies with time, t?

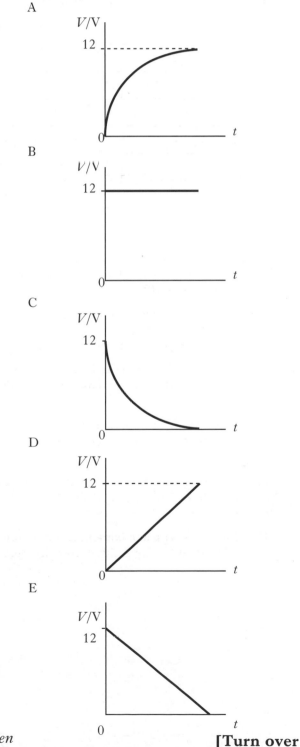

13. An op-amp is connected in a circuit as shown.

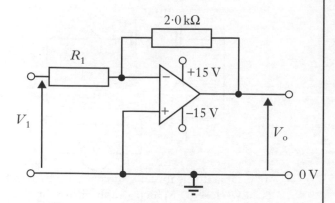

The input voltage V_1 is 0·50 V.

Which row in the table shows possible values for R_1 and V_o?

	$R_1/\text{k}\Omega$	V_o/V
A	1·0	1·0
B	4·0	1·0
C	1·0	−0·25
D	4·0	−1·0
E	1·0	−1·0

14. Photons of energy $7·0 \times 10^{-19}$ J are incident on a clean metal surface. The work function of the metal is $9·0 \times 10^{-19}$ J.

Which of the following is correct?

A No electrons are emitted from the metal.

B Electrons with a maximum kinetic energy of $2·0 \times 10^{-19}$ J are emitted from the metal.

C Electrons with a maximum kinetic energy of $7·0 \times 10^{-19}$ J are emitted from the metal.

D Electrons with a maximum kinetic energy of $9·0 \times 10^{-19}$ J are emitted from the metal.

E Electrons with a maximum kinetic energy of 16×10^{-19} J are emitted from the metal.

15. The diagram represents some of the energy levels for an atom of a gas.

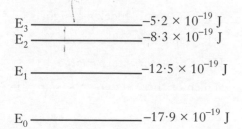

White light passes through the gas and absorption lines are observed in the spectrum.

Which electron transition produces the absorption line corresponding to the lowest frequency?

A E_3 to E_2

B E_2 to E_3

C E_1 to E_0

D E_0 to E_1

E E_0 to E_3

16. An LED is connected as shown.

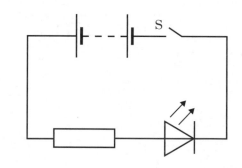

When switch S is closed

A the p-n junction is reverse biased and free charge carriers are produced which may recombine to give quanta of radiation

B the p-n junction is forward biased and positive and negative charge carriers are produced by the action of light

C the p-n junction is reverse biased and positive and negative charge carriers are produced by the action of light

D the p-n junction is forward biased and positive and negative charge carriers may recombine to give quanta of radiation

E the p-n junction is reverse biased and positive and negative charge carriers may recombine to give quanta of radiation.

17. The diagram represents the structure of an n-channel enhancement MOSFET.

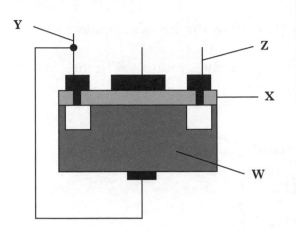

Which row in the table gives the names for the parts labelled **W**, **X**, **Y** and **Z**?

	W	X	Y	Z
A	substrate	implant	source	drain
B	implant	substrate	source	drain
C	substrate	oxide layer	drain	source
D	implant	substrate	gate	source
E	substrate	oxide layer	source	drain

18. The following statement describes a fusion reaction.

$$^{2}_{1}H + {}^{2}_{1}H \longrightarrow {}^{3}_{2}He + {}^{1}_{0}n + energy$$

The total mass of the particles before the reaction is $6 \cdot 684 \times 10^{-27}$ kg.

The total mass of the particles after the reaction is $6 \cdot 680 \times 10^{-27}$ kg.

The energy released in this reaction is

A $6 \cdot 012 \times 10^{-10}$ J

B $6 \cdot 016 \times 10^{-10}$ J

C $1 \cdot 800 \times 10^{-13}$ J

D $3 \cdot 600 \times 10^{-13}$ J

E $1 \cdot 200 \times 10^{-21}$ J.

19. A sample of tissue receives an equivalent dose of 40 mSv from a beam of neutrons.

The neutrons have a radiation weighting factor of 10.

The energy absorbed by the tissue is 100 µJ.

The mass of the tissue is

A $2 \cdot 5 \times 10^{-4}$ kg

B $2 \cdot 5 \times 10^{-2}$ kg

C $4 \cdot 0$ kg

D 40 kg

E $4 \cdot 0 \times 10^{3}$ kg.

20. A sample of tissue is placed near a source of gamma radiation. The equivalent dose rate for the tissue is 80 µSv h^{-1}.

The equivalent dose rate is now reduced to 10 µSv h^{-1} by placing lead shielding between the source and the tissue.

The half value thickness of lead is $8 \cdot 0$ mm for this source.

The thickness of the lead shielding is

A $1 \cdot 0$ mm

B $8 \cdot 0$ mm

C 24 mm

D 64 mm

E 80 mm.

[Turn over

Marks

SECTION B

Write your answers to questions 21 to 30 in the answer book.

21. A helicopter is flying at a constant height above the ground. The helicopter is carrying a crate suspended from a cable as shown.

(a) The helicopter flies 20 km on a bearing of 180 (due South). It then turns on to a bearing of 140 (50° South of East) and travels a further 30 km.

The helicopter takes 15 minutes to travel the 50 km.

   (i) By scale drawing (or otherwise) find the resultant displacement of the helicopter.   **2**

   (ii) Calculate the average velocity of the helicopter during the 15 minutes.   **2**

(b) The helicopter reaches its destination and hovers above a drop zone.

   (i) The total mass of the helicopter and crate is $1·21 \times 10^4$ kg.

        Show that the helicopter produces a lift force of 119 kN.   **1**

   (ii) The helicopter now drops the crate which has a mass of $2·30 \times 10^3$ kg. The lift force remains constant.

        Describe the vertical motion of the helicopter immediately after the crate is dropped.

        Justify your answer in terms of the forces acting on the helicopter.   **2**

                                                                                    (7)

Marks

22. The apparatus shown is set up to investigate collisions between two vehicles on a track.

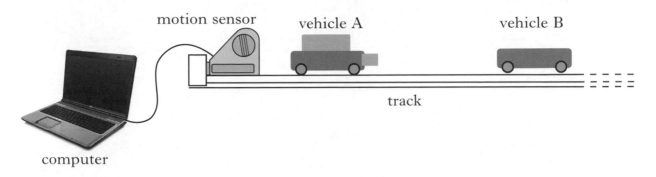

The mass of vehicle A is 0·22 kg and the mass of vehicle B is 0·16 kg.

The effects of friction are negligible.

(a) During one experiment the vehicles collide and stick together. The computer connected to the motion sensor displays the velocity-time graph for vehicle A.

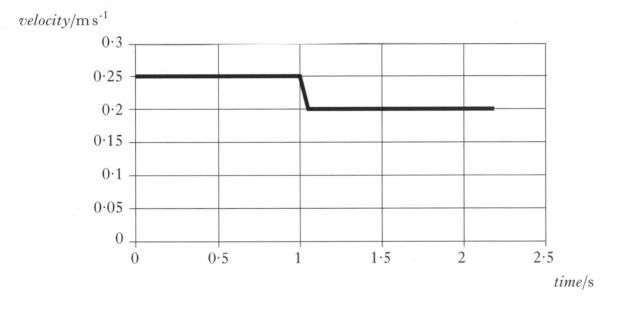

    (i) State the law of conservation of momentum.   **1**

    (ii) Calculate the velocity of vehicle B before the collision.   **2**

(b) The same apparatus is used to carry out a second experiment.

In this experiment, vehicle B is stationary before the collision.

Vehicle A has the same velocity before the collision as in the first experiment.

After the collision, the two vehicles stick together.

Is their combined velocity less than, equal to, or greater than that in the first collision?

Justify your answer.   **2**

     (5)

Marks

23. (*a*) A gymnast of mass 40 kg is practising on a trampoline.

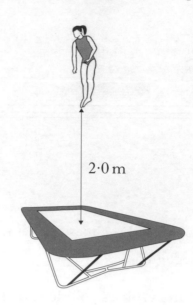

2·0 m

(i) At maximum height the gymnast's feet are 2·0 m above the trampoline. Show that the speed of the gymnast, as she lands on the trampoline, is 6·3 m s⁻¹.

1

(ii) The gymnast rebounds with a speed of 5·7 m s⁻¹. Calculate the change in momentum of the gymnast.

2

(iii) The gymnast was in contact with the trampoline for 0·50 s. Calculate the average force exerted by the trampoline on the gymnast.

2

Marks

23. (continued)

(b) Another gymnast is practising on a piece of equipment called the rings. The gymnast grips two wooden rings suspended above the gym floor by strong, vertical ropes as shown in Figure 1.

Figure 1

He now stretches out his arms until each rope makes an angle of 10° with the vertical as shown in Figure 2.

Figure 2

Explain why the tension in each rope increases as the gymnast stretches out his arms.

2

(7)

[Turn over

Marks

24. An experiment is carried out to measure the time taken for a steel ball to fall vertically through a fixed distance using an electronic timer.

    (a) The experiment is repeated and the following values for time recorded.

    0·49 s,   0·53 s,   0·50 s,   0·50 s,   0·55 s,   0·51 s.

    Calculate:

    (i)   the mean value of the time;   1

    (ii) the approximate random uncertainty in the mean value of the time.   1

    (b) Part of the circuit in the electronic timer consists of a 1·6 mF capacitor and an 18 kΩ resistor connected to a switch and a 4·5 V supply.

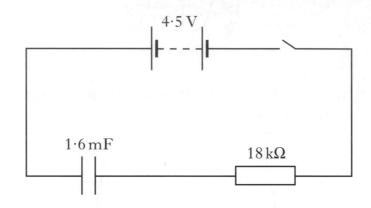

    (i)   Calculate the charge on the capacitor when it is fully charged.   2

    (ii) Sketch the graph of the current in the resistor against time as the capacitor charges.

    Numerical values are required on the current axis.   2

                                                                                 (6)

Marks

25. The headlights on a truck are switched on automatically when a light sensor detects the light level falling below a certain value.

   The light sensor consists of an LDR connected in a Wheatstone bridge as shown.

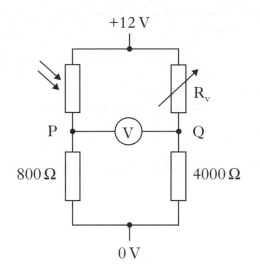

(a) The variable resistor, R_v, is set at $6000\,\Omega$.

   (i) Calculate the resistance of the LDR when the bridge is balanced.   2

   (ii) As the light level decreases, the resistance of the LDR increases. Calculate the reading on the voltmeter when the resistance of the LDR is $1600\,\Omega$.   2

(b) The Wheatstone bridge is connected to an op-amp as shown. The output of the op-amp controls the headlights circuit.

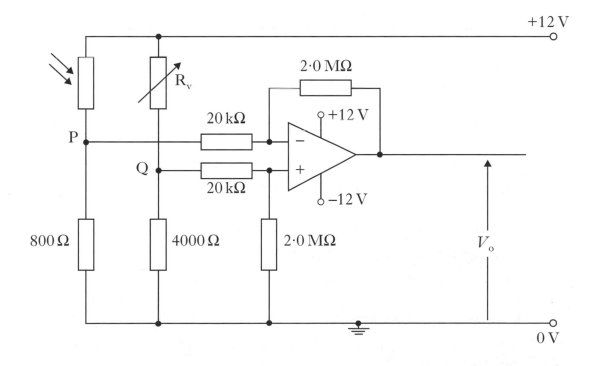

   The resistance of R_v is adjusted so that the potential at Q is $3.2\,V$. At a particular light level, the potential at P is $3.0\,V$. Determine the output voltage, V_o, of the op-amp.   3

   (7)

Marks

26. A signal generator is connected to a lamp, a resistor and an ammeter in series. An oscilloscope is connected across the output terminals of the signal generator.

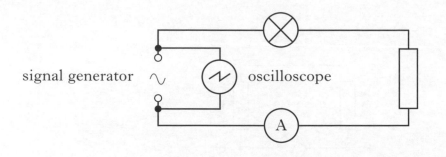

The oscilloscope control settings and the trace displayed on its screen are shown.

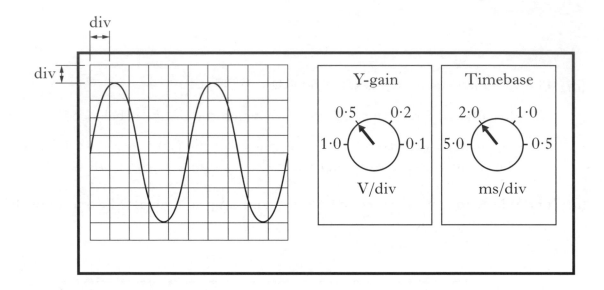

(a) For this signal calculate:

   (i) the peak voltage;   1

   (ii) the frequency.   2

(b) The frequency is now doubled. The peak voltage of the signal is kept constant.

   State what happens to the reading on the ammeter.   1

(c) The resistor is now replaced by a capacitor.

   The procedure in part (b) is repeated.

   State what happens to the reading on the ammeter as the frequency is doubled.   1

(d) The capacitor will be damaged if the potential difference across it exceeds 16 V.

   The capacitor is now removed from this circuit and connected to a different a.c. supply of output 15 V$_{r.m.s.}$.

   Explain whether or not the capacitor is damaged.   2

                                                                                                                    (7)

Marks

27. A student is carrying out an experiment to investigate the interference of sound waves. She sets up the following apparatus.

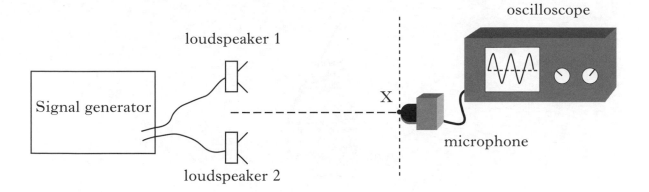

The microphone is initially placed at point X which is the same distance from each loudspeaker. A maximum is detected at X.

(*a*) The microphone is now moved to the first minimum at Y as shown.

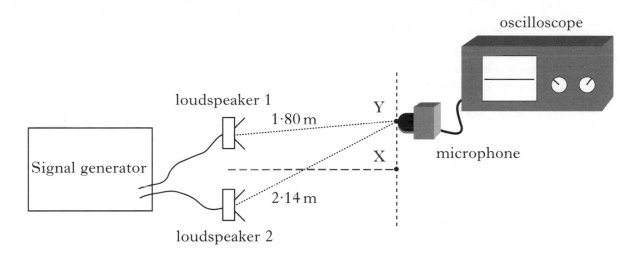

Calculate the wavelength of the sound waves.   2

(*b*) Loudspeaker 1 is now disconnected.

What happens to the amplitude of the sound detected by the microphone at Y?

Explain your answer.   2

(4)

[Turn over

Marks

28. A garden spray consists of a tank, a pump and a spray nozzle.

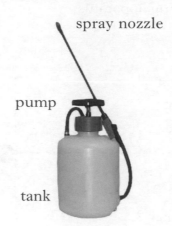

spray nozzle

pump

tank

The tank is partially filled with water.

The pump is then used to increase the pressure of the air above the water.

(a) The volume of the compressed air in the tank is $1{\cdot}60 \times 10^{-3}\,\mathrm{m}^3$.

The surface area of the water is $3{\cdot}00 \times 10^{-2}\,\mathrm{m}^2$.

The pressure of the air in the tank is $4{\cdot}60 \times 10^5\,\mathrm{Pa}$.

   (i) Calculate the force on the surface of the water.   2

  (ii) The spray nozzle is operated and water is pushed out until the pressure of the air in the tank is $1{\cdot}00 \times 10^5\,\mathrm{Pa}$.

Calculate the volume of water expelled.   3

(b) The gardener observes a spectrum when sunlight illuminates the drops of water in the spray. This is because each drop of water is acting as a prism.

The diagram shows the path taken by light of wavelength 650 nm through a drop of water.

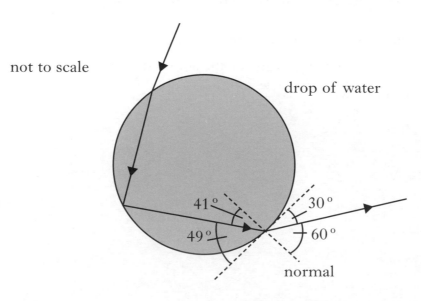

not to scale

drop of water

41°

30°

49°

60°

normal

   (i) What happens to the frequency of this light when it enters the drop of water?   1

Marks

28. (*b*) (continued)

(ii) Using information from the diagram, calculate the refractive index of the water for this wavelength of light.

2

(iii) Calculate the critical angle for this wavelength of light in the water.

2

(iv) Light of shorter wavelength also passes through the drop of water.

Will the critical angle for this light be less than, equal to, or greater than that for light of wavelength 650 nm?

Justify your answer.

2

(12)

[Turn over

Marks

29. A laser produces a beam of light with a frequency of $4{\cdot}74 \times 10^{14}\,\text{Hz}$.

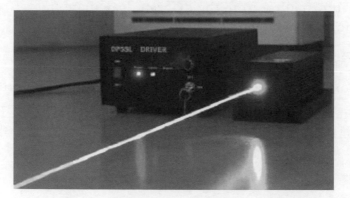

(a) The laser has a power of $0{\cdot}10\,\text{mW}$. Explain why light from this laser can cause eye damage.   1

(b) Calculate the energy of each photon in the laser beam.   2

(c) Inside the laser, photons stimulate the emission of more photons.

State **two** ways in which the stimulated photons are identical to the photons producing them.   1

(d) This laser beam is now incident on a grating as shown below.

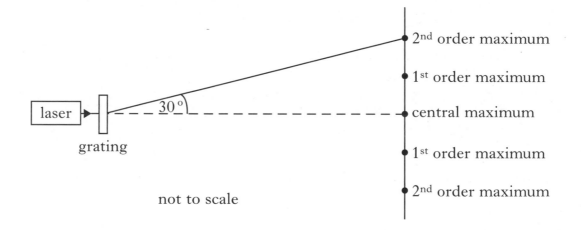

The second order maximum is detected at an angle of $30\,^\circ$ from the central maximum.

Calculate the separation of the slits on the grating.   3

(7)

Marks

30. A smoke alarm contains a very small sample of the radioactive isotope Americium-241, represented by the symbol

$$^{241}_{95}Am$$

(a) How many neutrons are there in a nucleus of this isotope?   1

(b) This isotope decays by emitting alpha particles as shown in the following statement.

$$^{241}_{95}Am \longrightarrow {}^{s}_{r}T + \alpha$$

   (i) Determine the numbers represented by the letters *r* and *s*.   1

   (ii) Use the data booklet to identify the element *T*.   1

(c) The activity of the radioactive sample is 30 kBq. How many decays take place in one minute?   2

(d) The alarm circuit in the smoke detector contains a battery of e.m.f. 9·0 V and internal resistance 2·0 Ω.

This circuit is shown.

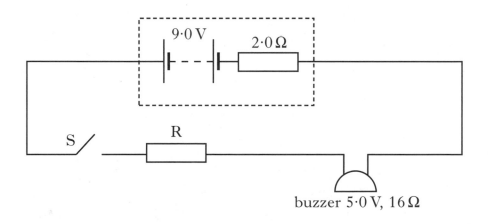

When smoke is detected, switch S closes and the buzzer operates. The buzzer has a resistance of 16 Ω and an operating voltage of 5·0 V.

Calculate the value of resistor R required in this circuit.   3

(8)

[END OF QUESTION PAPER]

[BLANK PAGE]

[BLANK PAGE]

X069/301

NATIONAL
QUALIFICATIONS
2011

MONDAY, 23 MAY
1.00 PM – 3.30 PM

PHYSICS
HIGHER

Read Carefully

Reference may be made to the Physics Data Booklet.

1 All questions should be attempted.

Section A (questions 1 to 20)

2 Check that the answer sheet is for Physics Higher (Section A).

3 For this section of the examination you must use an **HB pencil** and, where necessary, an eraser.

4 Check that the answer sheet you have been given has **your name**, **date of birth**, **SCN** (Scottish Candidate Number) and **Centre Name** printed on it.

   Do not change any of these details.

5 If any of this information is wrong, tell the Invigilator immediately.

6 If this information is correct, **print** your name and seat number in the boxes provided.

7 There is **only one correct** answer to each question.

8 Any rough working should be done on the question paper or the rough working sheet, **not** on your answer sheet.

9 At the end of the exam, put the **answer sheet for Section A inside the front cover of your answer book**.

10 Instructions as to how to record your answers to questions 1–20 are given on page three.

Section B (questions 21 to 30)

11 Answer the questions numbered 21 to 30 in the answer book provided.

12 **All answers must be written clearly and legibly in ink**.

13 Fill in the details on the front of the answer book.

14 Enter the question number clearly in the margin of the answer book beside each of your answers to questions 21 to 30.

15 Care should be taken to give an appropriate number of significant figures in the final answers to calculations.

16 Where additional paper, eg square ruled paper, is used, write your name and SCN (Scottish Candidate Number) on it and place it inside the front cover of your answer booklet.

DATA SHEET
COMMON PHYSICAL QUANTITIES

Quantity	Symbol	Value	Quantity	Symbol	Value
Speed of light in vacuum	c	$3 \cdot 00 \times 10^{8} \, \mathrm{m \, s^{-1}}$	Mass of electron	m_e	$9 \cdot 11 \times 10^{-31} \, \mathrm{kg}$
Magnitude of the charge on an electron	e	$1 \cdot 60 \times 10^{-19} \, \mathrm{C}$	Mass of neutron	m_n	$1 \cdot 675 \times 10^{-27} \, \mathrm{kg}$
Gravitational acceleration on Earth	g	$9 \cdot 8 \, \mathrm{m \, s^{-2}}$	Mass of proton	m_p	$1 \cdot 673 \times 10^{-27} \, \mathrm{kg}$
Planck's constant	h	$6 \cdot 63 \times 10^{-34} \, \mathrm{J \, s}$			

REFRACTIVE INDICES

The refractive indices refer to sodium light of wavelength 589 nm and to substances at a temperature of 273 K.

Substance	Refractive index	Substance	Refractive index
Diamond	2·42	Water	1·33
Crown glass	1·50	Air	1·00

SPECTRAL LINES

Element	Wavelength/nm	Colour	Element	Wavelength/nm	Colour
Hydrogen	656	Red	Cadmium	644	Red
	486	Blue-green		509	Green
	434	Blue-violet		480	Blue
	410	Violet		*Lasers*	
	397	Ultraviolet	Element	Wavelength/nm	Colour
	389	Ultraviolet	Carbon dioxide	9550 } 10590 }	Infrared
Sodium	589	Yellow	Helium-neon	633	Red

PROPERTIES OF SELECTED MATERIALS

Substance	Density/kg m^{-3}	Melting Point/K	Boiling Point/K
Aluminium	$2 \cdot 70 \times 10^{3}$	933	2623
Copper	$8 \cdot 96 \times 10^{3}$	1357	2853
Ice	$9 \cdot 20 \times 10^{2}$	273	. . . .
Sea Water	$1 \cdot 02 \times 10^{3}$	264	377
Water	$1 \cdot 00 \times 10^{3}$	273	373
Air	$1 \cdot 29$	. . . .	. . . .
Hydrogen	$9 \cdot 0 \times 10^{-2}$	14	20

The gas densities refer to a temperature of 273 K and a pressure of $1 \cdot 01 \times 10^{5}$ Pa.

SECTION A

For questions 1 to 20 in this section of the paper the answer to each question is either A, B, C, D or E. Decide what your answer is, then, using your pencil, put a horizontal line in the space provided—see the example below.

EXAMPLE

The energy unit measured by the electricity meter in your home is the

 A kilowatt-hour

 B ampere

 C watt

 D coulomb

 E volt.

The correct answer is **A**—kilowatt-hour. The answer **A** has been clearly marked in **pencil** with a horizontal line (see below).

Changing an answer

If you decide to change your answer, carefully erase your first answer and, using your pencil, fill in the answer you want. The answer below has been changed to **E**.

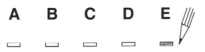

[Turn over

SECTION A

Answer questions 1–20 on the answer sheet.

1. Which of the following is a scalar quantity?

   A   velocity

   B   acceleration

   C   mass

   D   force

   E   momentum

2. A vehicle is travelling in a straight line. Graphs of velocity and acceleration against time are shown.

   Which pair of graphs could represent the motion of the vehicle?

   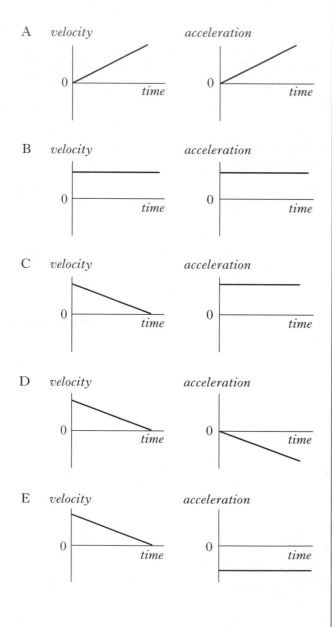

3. A car of mass 1200 kg pulls a horsebox of mass 700 kg along a straight, horizontal road.

   They have an acceleration of $2 \cdot 0 \, \text{m s}^{-2}$.

   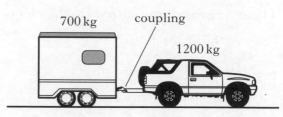

   Assuming that the frictional forces are negligible, the tension in the coupling between the car and the horsebox is

   A   500 N

   B   700 N

   C   1400 N

   D   2400 N

   E   3800 N.

4. Two trolleys travel towards each other in a straight line along a frictionless surface.

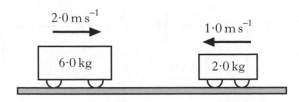

The trolleys collide. After the collision the trolleys move as shown below.

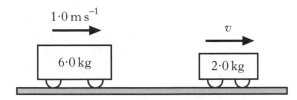

Which row in the table gives the total momentum and the total kinetic energy **after** the collision?

	Total momentum/ $\mathrm{kg\,m\,s^{-1}}$	Total kinetic energy/ J
A	10	7·0
B	10	13
C	10	20
D	14	13
E	14	7·0

5. An aircraft cruises at an altitude at which the external air pressure is $0·40 \times 10^5\,\mathrm{Pa}$. The air pressure inside the aircraft cabin is maintained at $1·0 \times 10^5\,\mathrm{Pa}$. The area of an external cabin door is $2·0\,\mathrm{m}^2$.

What is the outward force on the door due to the pressure difference?

A $0·30 \times 10^5\,\mathrm{N}$

B $0·70 \times 10^5\,\mathrm{N}$

C $1·2 \times 10^5\,\mathrm{N}$

D $2·0 \times 10^5\,\mathrm{N}$

E $2·8 \times 10^5\,\mathrm{N}$

6. A cylinder of height $1·0\,\mathrm{m}$ is held stationary in a swimming pool. The top of the cylinder is at a depth of $1·5\,\mathrm{m}$ below the surface of the water.

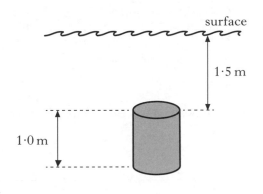

The density of the water is $1·0 \times 10^3\,\mathrm{kg\,m^{-3}}$.

The pressure due to the water exerted on the top surface of the cylinder is

A $1·5 \times 10^3\,\mathrm{N\,m^{-2}}$

B $4·9 \times 10^3\,\mathrm{N\,m^{-2}}$

C $9·8 \times 10^3\,\mathrm{N\,m^{-2}}$

D $14·7 \times 10^3\,\mathrm{N\,m^{-2}}$

E $24·5 \times 10^3\,\mathrm{N\,m^{-2}}$.

7. A fixed mass of gas is heated inside a rigid container. As its temperature changes from T_1 to T_2 the pressure increases from $1·0 \times 10^5\,\mathrm{Pa}$ to $2·0 \times 10^5\,\mathrm{Pa}$.

Which row in the table shows possible values for T_1 and T_2?

	T_1	T_2
A	27 °C	327 °C
B	30 °C	60 °C
C	80 °C	40 °C
D	303 K	333 K
E	600 K	300 K

[Turn over

8. One volt is equivalent to one

   A   farad per coulomb

   B   ampere per ohm

   C   joule per ampere

   D   joule per ohm

   E   joule per coulomb.

9. A Wheatstone bridge circuit is set up as shown.

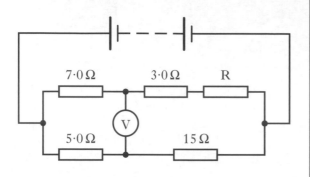

   The reading on the voltmeter is zero.

   The value of resistor R is

   A $3 \cdot 0 \, \Omega$

   B $4 \cdot 0 \, \Omega$

   C $18 \, \Omega$

   D $21 \, \Omega$

   E $24 \, \Omega$.

10. A Wheatstone bridge circuit is set up as shown.

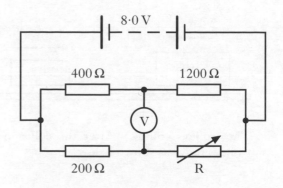

   When the variable resistor R is set at $600 \, \Omega$ the bridge is balanced. When R is set at $601 \, \Omega$ the reading on the voltmeter is $+2 \cdot 5 \, \text{mV}$.

   R is now set at $598 \, \Omega$.

   The reading on the voltmeter is

   A $-7 \cdot 5 \, \text{mV}$

   B $-5 \cdot 0 \, \text{mV}$

   C $-2 \cdot 5 \, \text{mV}$

   D $+5 \cdot 0 \, \text{mV}$

   E $+7 \cdot 5 \, \text{mV}$.

11. The output of a 50 Hz a.c. supply is connected to the input of an oscilloscope. The trace produced on the screen of the oscilloscope is shown.

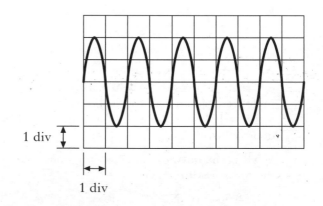

   The time-base control of the oscilloscope is set at

   A   1 ms/div

   B   10 ms/div

   C   20 ms/div

   D   100 ms/div

   E   200 ms/div.

12. An a.c. supply with an output voltage of 6·0 V r.m.s. is connected to a 3·0 Ω resistor.

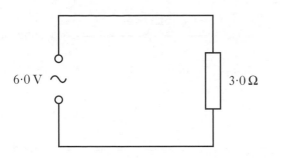

6·0 V   ∿   3·0 Ω

Which row in the table shows the peak voltage across the resistor and the peak current in the circuit?

	Peak voltage/V	Peak current/A
A	$6\sqrt{2}$	$2\sqrt{2}$
B	$6\sqrt{2}$	2
C	6	2
D	$\dfrac{6}{\sqrt{2}}$	$\dfrac{2}{\sqrt{2}}$
E	6	$2\sqrt{2}$

13. In an experiment to find the capacitance of a capacitor, a student makes the following measurements.

potential difference across capacitor $= (10\cdot0 \pm 0\cdot1)$ V

charge stored by capacitor $= (500 \pm 25)\,\mu$C

Which row in the table gives the capacitance of the capacitor and the percentage uncertainty in the capacitance?

	Capacitance/μF	Percentage uncertainty
A	0·02	1
B	0·02	5
C	50	1
D	50	5
E	5000	6

14. A capacitor is connected to an a.c. supply and a.c. ammeter as shown.

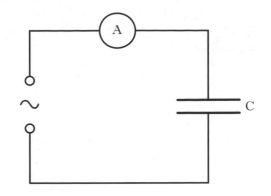

The supply has a constant peak voltage, but its frequency can be varied.

Which graph shows how the current I varies with the frequency f of the supply?

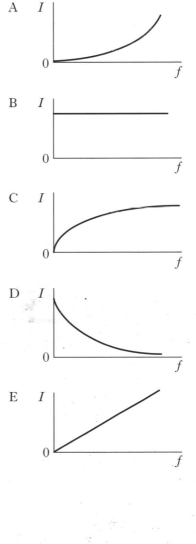

[Turn over

15. Two identical loudspeakers, L_1 and L_2, are connected to a signal generator as shown.

signal generator

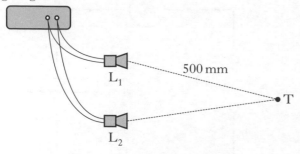

An interference pattern is produced.

A minimum is detected at point T.

The wavelength of the sound is 40 mm.

The distance from L_1 to T is 500 mm.

The distance from L_2 to T is

A   450 mm

B   460 mm

C   470 mm

D   480 mm

E   490 mm.

16. The irradiance of light from a point source is $20\,\mathrm{W\,m^{-2}}$ at a distance of $5{\cdot}0\,\mathrm{m}$ from the source.

What is the irradiance of the light at a distance of 25 m from the source?

A $0{\cdot}032\,\mathrm{W\,m^{-2}}$

B $0{\cdot}80\,\mathrm{W\,m^{-2}}$

C $4{\cdot}0\,\mathrm{W\,m^{-2}}$

D $100\,\mathrm{W\,m^{-2}}$

E $500\,\mathrm{W\,m^{-2}}$

17. The diagram below represents part of the process of stimulated emission in a laser.

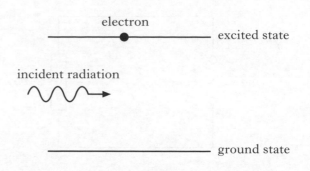

Which statement best describes the emitted radiation?

A   Out of phase and emitted in the same direction as the incident radiation.

B   Out of phase and emitted in the opposite direction to the incident radiation.

C   Out of phase and emitted in all directions.

D   In phase and emitted in the same direction as the incident radiation.

E   In phase and emitted in the opposite direction to the incident radiation.

18. In an n-type semiconductor

A   the majority charge carriers are electrons

B   the majority charge carriers are holes

C   the majority charge carriers are protons

D   there are more protons than electrons

E   there are more electrons than protons.

19. The following statement represents a nuclear decay.

$$^{214}_{x}\text{Pb} \rightarrow {}^{y}_{83}\text{Bi} + {}^{o}_{z}\text{e}$$

Which row in the table shows the correct values of x, y and z for this decay?

	x	y	z
A	82	210	−1
B	82	214	−1
C	84	214	1
D	85	210	2
E	85	214	2

20. The graph shows how the corrected count rate from a radioactive source varies with the thickness of a material placed between the source and a detector.

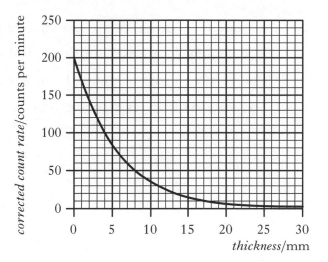

The half value thickness of the material is

A   4 mm

B   14 mm

C   28 mm

D   100 mm

E   200 mm.

[Turn over

SECTION B

Marks

Write your answers to questions 21 to 30 in the answer book.

21. A student investigates the motion of a ball projected from a launcher.

    The launcher is placed on the ground and a ball is fired vertically upwards.

    The vertical speed of the ball as it leaves the top of the launcher is $7 \cdot 0 \, \text{m s}^{-1}$.

    The effects of air resistance can be ignored.

    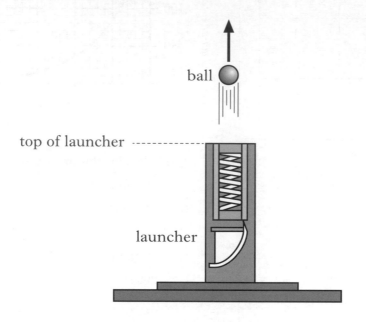

    (*a*) (i) Calculate the maximum height above the top of the launcher reached by the ball. 2

    (ii) Show that the time taken for the ball to reach its maximum height is $0 \cdot 71 \, \text{s}$. 1

Marks

21. (continued)

(b) The student now fixes the launcher to a trolley. The trolley travels horizontally at a constant speed of $1 \cdot 5 \, \text{m s}^{-1}$ to the right.

The launcher again fires the ball vertically upwards with a speed of $7 \cdot 0 \, \text{m s}^{-1}$.

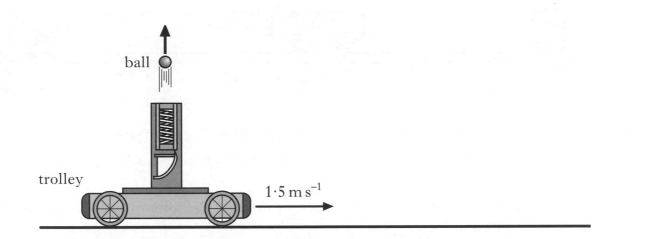

(i) Determine the velocity of the ball after $0 \cdot 71 \, \text{s}$.   **1**

(ii) The student asks some friends to predict where the ball will land relative to the moving launcher. They make the following statements.

Statement X: *The ball will land behind the launcher.*

Statement Y: *The ball will land in front of the launcher.*

Statement Z: *The ball will land on top of the launcher.*

Which of the statements is correct?

You must justify your answer.   **2**

      (6)

[Turn over

22. An experiment is set up to investigate the motion of a cart as it collides with a force sensor.

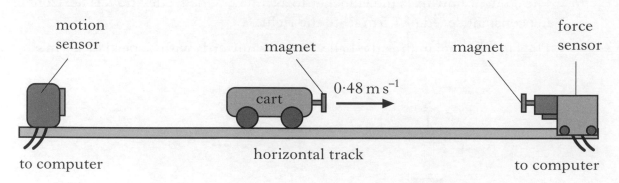

to computer   horizontal track   to computer

The cart moves along the horizontal track at $0.48 \, \text{m s}^{-1}$ to the right.

As the cart approaches the force sensor, the magnets repel each other and exert a force on the cart.

The computer attached to the force sensor displays the following force-time graph for this collision.

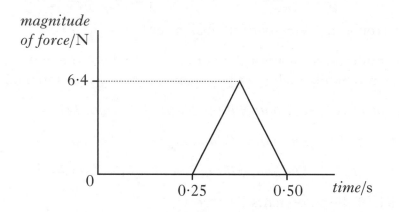

The computer attached to the motion sensor displays the following velocity-time graph for the cart.

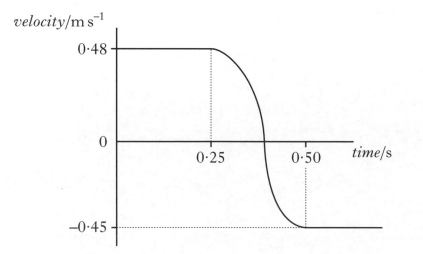

Marks

22. (continued)

   (*a*)   (i)   Calculate the magnitude of the impulse on the cart during the collision.   **2**

        (ii)   Determine the magnitude and direction of the change in momentum of the cart.   **1**

       (iii)   Calculate the mass of the cart.   **2**

   (*b*)   The experiment is repeated using different magnets which produce a greater average force on the cart during the collision. As before, the cart is initially travelling at $0.48 \, \text{m s}^{-1}$ to the right and the collision causes the same change in its velocity.

       Copy the force-time graph shown and, on the same axes, draw another graph to show how the magnitude of the force varies with time in this collision.

       Numerical values are not required but you must label each graph clearly.   **2**

                                             (7)

[Turn over

Marks

23. A technician uses the equipment shown to calculate a value for the density of air at room temperature.

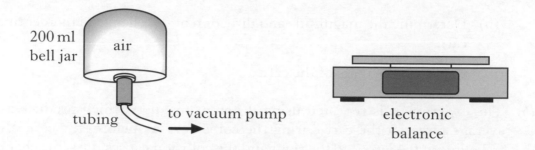

200 ml bell jar   air

tubing   to vacuum pump   electronic balance

The mass of the bell jar is measured when it is full of air. The vacuum pump is then used to remove air from the bell jar. The mass of the bell jar is measured again.

The following measurements are obtained.

> Mass before air is removed = 111·49 g
>
> Mass after air is removed = 111·26 g
>
> Volume of bell jar   = 200 ml = $2·0 \times 10^{-4}\,\text{m}^3$

(a)   (i)   Use these measurements to calculate a value for the density of air in kg m^{-3}.   **2**

      (ii)   The accepted value for the density of air at this temperature is $1·29\,\text{kg m}^{-3}$. Explain why the technician's answer is different from the accepted value.   **1**

(b)   Air is allowed back into the bell jar until it reaches a pressure of $1·01 \times 10^5\,\text{Pa}$.

The technician now uses a syringe to remove 50 ml of the air from the bell jar.

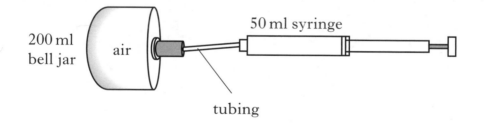

200 ml bell jar   air   50 ml syringe

tubing

The temperature of the air remains constant.

   (i)   Calculate the new pressure of the air inside the bell jar.   **2**

   (ii)   Use the kinetic model to explain this change in pressure after removing air with the syringe.   **2**

                   (7)

Marks

24. (*a*) A supply of e.m.f. 10·0 V and internal resistance *r* is connected in a circuit as shown in Figure 1.

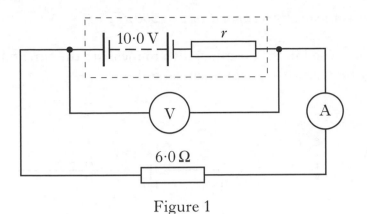

Figure 1

The meters display the following readings.

Reading on ammeter = 1·25 A

Reading on voltmeter = 7·50 V

   (i) What is meant by an *e.m.f. of 10·0 V*?   1

  (ii) Show that the internal resistance, *r*, of the supply is 2·0 Ω.   1

(*b*) A resistor R is connected to the circuit as shown in Figure 2.

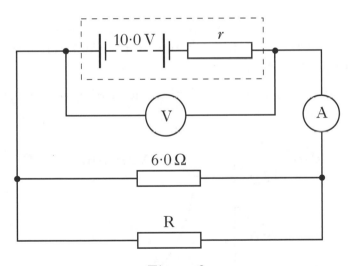

Figure 2

The meters now display the following readings.

Reading on ammeter = 2·0 A

Reading on voltmeter = 6·0 V

   (i) Explain why the reading on the voltmeter has decreased.   2

  (ii) Calculate the resistance of resistor R.   3

                                 (7)

Marks

25. A student carries out an experiment using a circuit which includes a capacitor with a capacitance of $200\,\mu\text{F}$.

    (*a*) Explain what is meant by a *capacitance of $200\,\mu\text{F}$*.   **1**

    (*b*) The capacitor is used in the circuit shown to measure the time taken for a ball to fall vertically between two strips of metal foil.

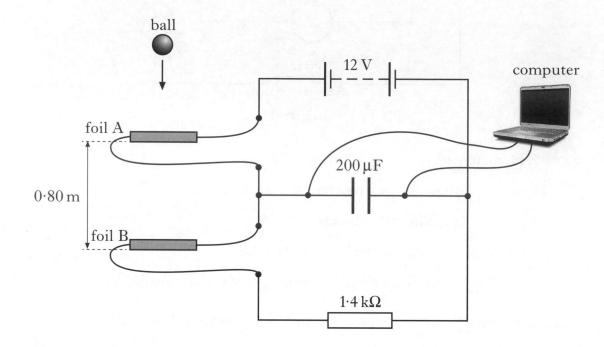

The ball is dropped from rest above foil A. It is travelling at $1\cdot5\,\text{m s}^{-1}$ when it reaches foil A. It breaks foil A, then a short time later breaks foil B. These strips of foil are $0\cdot80\,\text{m}$ apart.

The computer displays a graph of potential difference across the capacitor against time as shown.

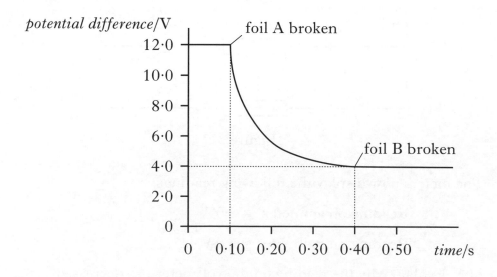

    (i) Calculate the current in the $1\cdot4\,\text{k}\Omega$ resistor at the moment foil A is broken.   **2**

    (ii) Calculate the **decrease** in the energy stored in the capacitor during the time taken for the ball to fall from foil A to foil B.   **3**

Marks

25. (continued)

(*c*) The measurements from this experiment are now used to estimate the acceleration due to gravity.

    (i) What is the time taken for the ball to fall from foil A to foil B?　　　1

    (ii) Use the results of this experiment to calculate a value for the acceleration due to gravity.　　　2

   (iii) The distance between the two foils is now increased and the experiment repeated. Explain why this gives a more accurate result for the acceleration due to gravity.　　　1

(10)

[Turn over

Marks

26.   (a) An op-amp is connected in a circuit as shown.

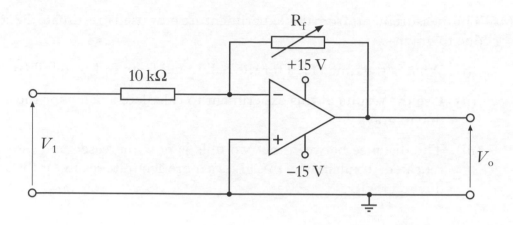

The resistance of the feedback resistor R_f is varied between $20\,k\Omega$ and $120\,k\Omega$.

The graph shows how the output voltage V_o varies as the resistance of the feedback resistor is increased.

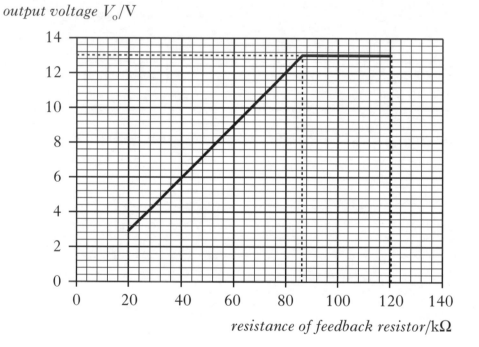

(i)   In which mode is the op-amp being used? 1

(ii) Calculate the input voltage V_1. 2

(iii) Explain why the output voltage V_o does not increase above 13 V. 1

Marks

26. (continued)

(b) The op-amp is now connected in a different circuit as shown.

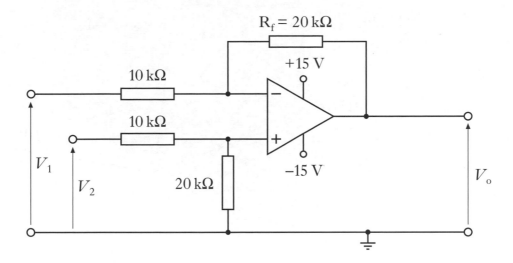

The input voltages V_1 and V_2 are now varied and the corresponding output voltage V_o is measured.

Graph 1 shows the input voltage V_1 for the first 3 seconds.

Graph 2 shows the input voltage V_2 for the first 3 seconds.

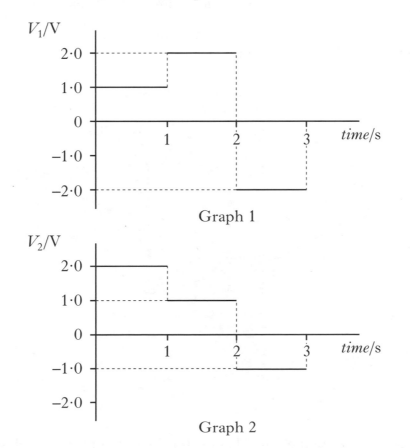

Graph 1

Graph 2

Sketch a graph to show the output voltage V_o from the op-amp for the first 3 seconds.

Numerical values are required on both the voltage and time axes.

3

(7)

Marks

27. (*a*) A ray of red light is incident on a block of glass as shown.

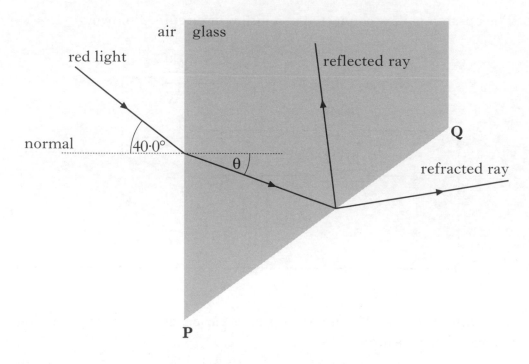

The refractive index of the glass for this light is 1·66.

   (i) Calculate the value of the angle θ shown in the diagram.   2

  (ii) The direction of the incident light ray is now changed so that the refracted ray emerges along face **PQ** as shown.

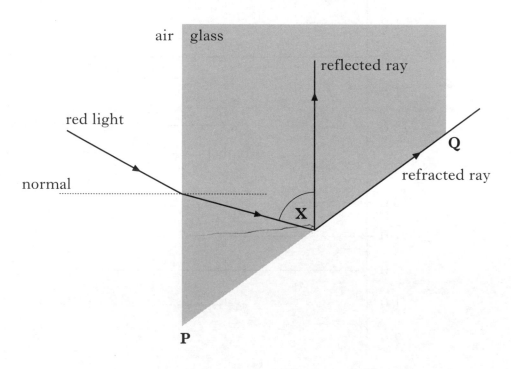

   (A) Calculate the critical angle for the red light in this glass.   2

   (B) Determine the size of angle **X** shown in the diagram.   1

Marks

27. (continued)

(b) The ray of red light is now replaced with a ray of blue light.

This ray of blue light is directed towards the block along the same path as the ray of red light in part (*a*)(ii).

Is this ray of blue light refracted at face **PQ**?

Justify your answer.   2

(7)

[Turn over

Marks

28. (*a*) The first demonstration of the interference of light was performed by Thomas Young in 1801.

What does the demonstration of interference prove about light?   **1**

(*b*) A grating is placed in a colourless liquid in a container. Laser light is incident on the grating along the normal. The spacing between the lines on the grating is $5 \cdot 0 \times 10^{-6}$ m. Interference occurs and the maxima produced are shown in the diagram.

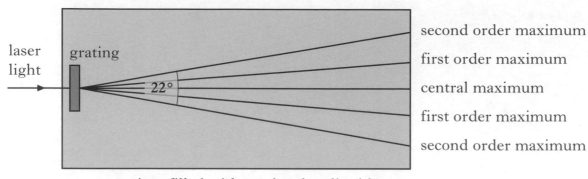

container filled with a colourless liquid

(i) Calculate the wavelength of the laser light in the liquid.   **2**

(ii) The refractive index of the colourless liquid decreases as the temperature of the liquid increases.

The liquid is now heated.

What effect does this have on the spacing between the maxima?

You must justify your answer.   **2**

(5)

29. A metal plate emits electrons when certain wavelengths of electromagnetic radiation are incident on it.

Marks

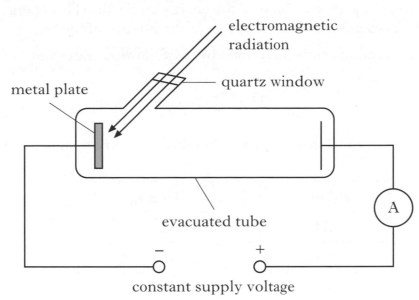

The work function of the metal is $2 \cdot 24 \times 10^{-19}$ J.

(a) Electrons arc released when electromagnetic radiation of wavelength 525 nm is incident on the surface of the metal plate.

(i) Show that the energy of each photon of the incident radiation is $3 \cdot 79 \times 10^{-19}$ J.   2

(ii) Calculate the maximum kinetic energy of an electron released from the surface of the metal plate.   1

(b) The frequency of the incident radiation is now varied through a range of values.

The maximum kinetic energy of electrons leaving the metal plate is determined for each frequency.

A graph of this maximum kinetic energy against frequency is shown.

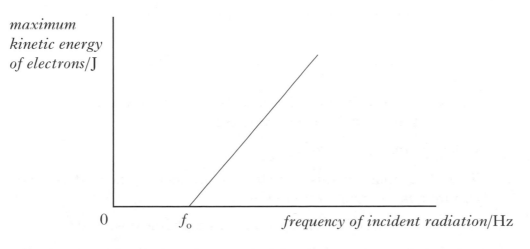

(i) Explain why the kinetic energy of the electrons is zero below the frequency f_o.   1

(ii) Calculate the value of the frequency f_o.   2

(6)

[Turn over for Question 30 on *Page twenty-four*

Marks

30. (*a*) The Sun is the source of most of the energy on Earth. This energy is produced by nuclear reactions which take place in the interior of the Sun.

One such reaction can be described by the following statement.

$$^{3}_{1}H + {}^{2}_{1}H \rightarrow {}^{4}_{2}He + {}^{1}_{0}n$$

The masses of the particles involved in this reaction are shown in the table.

Particle	Mass/kg
$^{3}_{1}H$	$5{\cdot}005 \times 10^{-27}$
$^{2}_{1}H$	$3{\cdot}342 \times 10^{-27}$
$^{4}_{2}He$	$6{\cdot}642 \times 10^{-27}$
$^{1}_{0}n$	$1{\cdot}675 \times 10^{-27}$

   (i) Name this type of nuclear reaction.   **1**

   (ii) Calculate the energy released in this reaction.   **3**

(*b*) The Sun emits a continuous spectrum of visible light. When this light passes through hydrogen atoms in the Sun's outer atmosphere, certain wavelengths are absorbed.

The diagram shows some of the energy levels for the hydrogen atom.

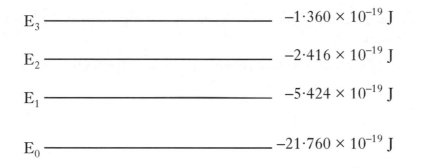

E_3	$-1{\cdot}360 \times 10^{-19}$ J
E_2	$-2{\cdot}416 \times 10^{-19}$ J
E_1	$-5{\cdot}424 \times 10^{-19}$ J
E_0	$-21{\cdot}760 \times 10^{-19}$ J

   (i) One of the wavelengths absorbed by the hydrogen atoms results in an electron transition from energy level E_1 to E_3.

Calculate this wavelength.   **3**

   (ii) The absorption of this wavelength produces a faint dark line in the continuous spectrum from the Sun.

In which colour of the spectrum is this dark line observed?   **1**

(8)

[*END OF QUESTION PAPER*]

HIGHER

2012

[BLANK PAGE]

X069/12/02

NATIONAL QUALIFICATIONS 2012	MONDAY, 28 MAY 1.00 PM – 3.30 PM	PHYSICS HIGHER

Read Carefully

Reference may be made to the Physics Data Booklet.

1   All questions should be attempted.

Section A (questions 1 to 20)

2   Check that the answer sheet is for Physics Higher (Section A).

3   For this section of the examination you must use an **HB pencil** and, where necessary, an eraser.

4   Check that the answer sheet you have been given has **your name**, **date of birth**, **SCN** (Scottish Candidate Number) and **Centre Name** printed on it.

Do not change any of these details.

5   If any of this information is wrong, tell the Invigilator immediately.

6   If this information is correct, **print** your name and seat number in the boxes provided.

7   There is **only one correct** answer to each question.

8   Any rough working should be done on the question paper or the rough working sheet, **not** on your answer sheet.

9   At the end of the exam, put the **answer sheet for Section A inside the front cover of your answer book**.

10   Instructions as to how to record your answers to questions 1–20 are given on page three.

Section B (questions 21 to 31)

11   Answer the questions numbered 21 to 31 in the answer book provided.

12   **All answers must be written clearly and legibly in ink**.

13   Fill in the details on the front of the answer book.

14   Enter the question number clearly in the margin of the answer book beside each of your answers to questions 21 to 31.

15   Care should be taken to give an appropriate number of significant figures in the final answers to calculations.

16   Where additional paper, eg square ruled paper, is used, write your name and SCN (Scottish Candidate Number) on it and place it inside the front cover of your answer booklet.

DATA SHEET
COMMON PHYSICAL QUANTITIES

Quantity	Symbol	Value	Quantity	Symbol	Value
Speed of light in vacuum	c	$3 \cdot 00 \times 10^8 \, \mathrm{m\,s^{-1}}$	Mass of electron	m_e	$9 \cdot 11 \times 10^{-31} \, \mathrm{kg}$
Magnitude of the charge on an electron	e	$1 \cdot 60 \times 10^{-19} \, \mathrm{C}$	Mass of neutron	m_n	$1 \cdot 675 \times 10^{-27} \, \mathrm{kg}$
Gravitational acceleration on Earth	g	$9 \cdot 8 \, \mathrm{m\,s^{-2}}$	Mass of proton	m_p	$1 \cdot 673 \times 10^{-27} \, \mathrm{kg}$
Planck's constant	h	$6 \cdot 63 \times 10^{-34} \, \mathrm{J\,s}$			

REFRACTIVE INDICES

The refractive indices refer to sodium light of wavelength 589 nm and to substances at a temperature of 273 K.

Substance	Refractive index	Substance	Refractive index
Diamond	2·42	Water	1·33
Crown glass	1·50	Air	1·00

SPECTRAL LINES

Element	Wavelength/nm	Colour	Element	Wavelength/nm	Colour
Hydrogen	656	Red	Cadmium	644	Red
	486	Blue-green		509	Green
	434	Blue-violet		480	Blue
	410	Violet		Lasers	
	397	Ultraviolet	Element	Wavelength/nm	Colour
	389	Ultraviolet	Carbon dioxide	9550 } 10590 }	Infrared
Sodium	589	Yellow	Helium-neon	633	Red

PROPERTIES OF SELECTED MATERIALS

Substance	Density/kg m^{-3}	Melting Point/K	Boiling Point/K
Aluminium	$2 \cdot 70 \times 10^3$	933	2623
Copper	$8 \cdot 96 \times 10^3$	1357	2853
Ice	$9 \cdot 20 \times 10^2$	273	. . . .
Sea Water	$1 \cdot 02 \times 10^3$	264	377
Water	$1 \cdot 00 \times 10^3$	273	373
Air	$1 \cdot 29$	. . . .	. . . .
Hydrogen	$9 \cdot 0 \ \times 10^{-2}$	14	20

The gas densities refer to a temperature of 273 K and a pressure of $1 \cdot 01 \times 10^5 \, \mathrm{Pa}$.

SECTION A

For questions 1 to 20 in this section of the paper the answer to each question is either A, B, C, D or E. Decide what your answer is, then, using your pencil, put a horizontal line in the space provided—see the example below.

EXAMPLE

The energy unit measured by the electricity meter in your home is the

    A kilowatt-hour

    B ampere

    C watt

    D coulomb

    E volt.

The correct answer is **A**—kilowatt-hour. The answer **A** has been clearly marked in **pencil** with a horizontal line (see below).

Changing an answer

If you decide to change your answer, carefully erase your first answer and, using your pencil, fill in the answer you want. The answer below has been changed to **E**.

[Turn over

SECTION A

Answer questions 1–20 on the answer sheet.

1. Which of the following contains one vector and two scalar quantities?

   A   force, time and acceleration

   B   power, momentum and velocity

   C   acceleration, velocity and force

   D   mass, distance and speed

   E   acceleration, time and speed

2. A trolley travels along a straight track.

   The graph shows how the velocity v of the trolley varies with time t.

   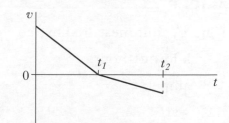

   Which graph shows how the acceleration a of the trolley varies with time t?

   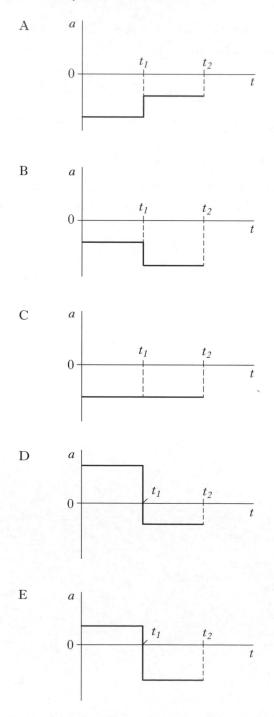

3. A rocket of mass 200 kg accelerates vertically upwards from the surface of a planet at $2\cdot0\,\text{m s}^{-2}$.

   The gravitational field strength on the planet is $4\cdot0\,\text{N kg}^{-1}$.

   What is the size of the force being exerted by the rocket's engines?

   A   400 N

   B   800 N

   C   1200 N

   D   2000 N

   E   2400 N

4. The diagram shows the masses and velocities of two trolleys just before they collide on a level bench.

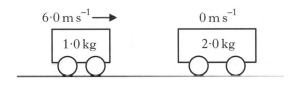

   After the collision, the trolleys move along the bench joined together.

   How much kinetic energy is lost in this collision?

   A   0 J

   B $6\cdot0$ J

   C   12 J

   D   18 J

   E   24 J

5. A fixed mass of gas condenses at atmospheric pressure to form a liquid.

   Which row in the table shows the approximate increase in density and the approximate decrease in spacing between molecules?

	Approximate increase in density	Approximate decrease in spacing between molecules
A	10 times	10 times
B	10 times	1000 times
C	1000 times	10 times
D	1000 times	1000 times
E	1 000 000 times	1000 times

6. Two identical blocks are suspended in water at different depths as shown.

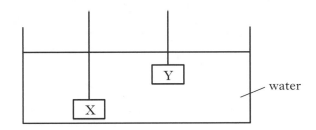

   A student makes the following statements.

   I   The buoyancy force on block Y is greater than the buoyancy force on block X.

   II   The pressure on the bottom of block X is greater than the pressure on the bottom of block Y.

   III The pressure on the top of block X is greater than the pressure on the top of block Y.

   Which of the statements is/are correct?

   A   I only

   B   II only

   C   I and II only

   D   II and III only

   E   I, II and III

   [Turn over

7. Which of the following graphs shows the relationship between the pressure P and the volume V of a fixed mass of gas at constant temperature?

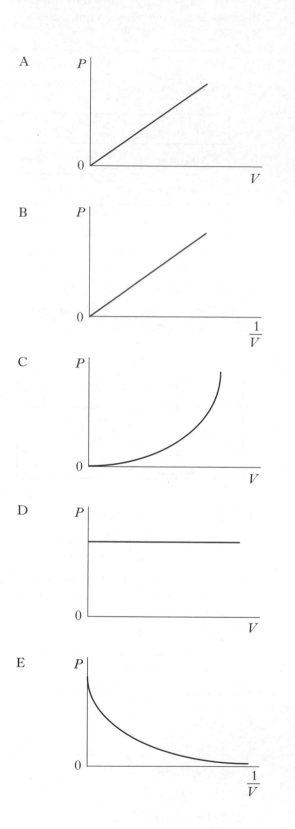

8. A circuit is set up as shown.

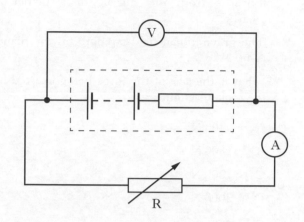

The variable resistor R is adjusted and a series of readings taken from the voltmeter and ammeter.

The graph shows how the voltmeter reading varies with the ammeter reading.

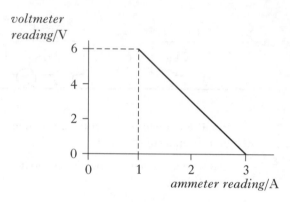

Which row in the table shows the values for the e.m.f. and internal resistance of the battery in the circuit?

	e.m.f./V	internal resistance/Ω
A	6	2
B	6	3
C	9	2
D	9	3
E	9	6

9. The diagram shows part of an electrical circuit.

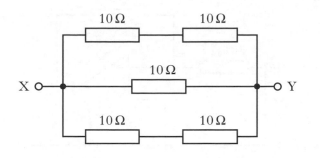

What is the resistance between X and Y?

A   0·2 Ω

B   5 Ω

C   10 Ω

D   20 Ω

E   50 Ω

10. An alternating voltage is displayed on an oscilloscope screen. The Y-gain and the timebase settings are shown.

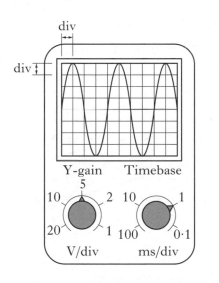

Which row in the table gives the values for the peak voltage and frequency of the signal?

	Peak voltage/V	Frequency/Hz
A	10	100
B	10	250
C	20	250
D	10	500
E	20	1000

11. A student carries out an experiment to find the capacitance of a capacitor. The charge on the capacitor is measured for different values of p.d. across the capacitor. The results are shown.

charge on capacitor/μC	p.d. across capacitor/V
1·9	1·0
4·6	2·0
9·6	4·0

The best estimate of the capacitance is

A   1·9 μF

B   2·2 μF

C   2·3 μF

D   2·4 μF

E   2·6 μF.

[Turn over

12. The circuits below have identical a.c. supplies which are set at a frequency of 200 Hz.

constant amplitude
variable frequency

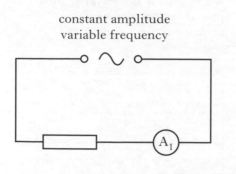

constant amplitude
variable frequency

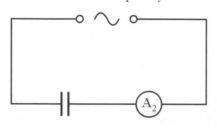

The frequency of each a.c. supply is now increased to 500 Hz.

What happens to the readings on the ammeters A_1 and A_2?

	A_1	A_2
A	increases	decreases
B	decreases	increases
C	no change	no change
D	no change	decreases
E	no change	increases

13. An op-amp circuit is set up as shown.

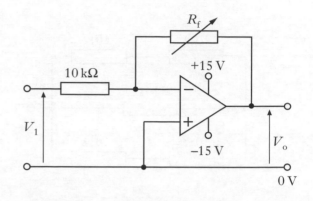

The resistance of R_f can be varied between 0 and 100 kΩ.

When the input voltage V_1 is +2 V a possible value of the output voltage V_o is

A   +20 V

B   +10 V

C   +2 V

D   −10 V

E   −20 V.

14. S_1 and S_2 are sources of coherent waves.

An interference pattern is obtained between X and Y.

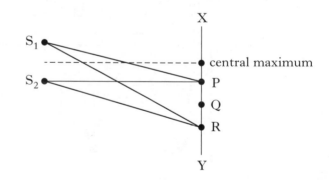

The first order maximum occurs at P, where $S_1P = 200$ mm and $S_2P = 180$ mm.

For the third order maximum, at R, the path difference $(S_1R - S_2R)$ is

A   20 mm

B   30 mm

C   40 mm

D   50 mm

E   60 mm.

15. Clean zinc plates are mounted on insulating handles and then charged.

Different types of electromagnetic radiation are now incident on the plates as shown.

Which of the zinc plates is most likely to discharge due to photoelectric emission?

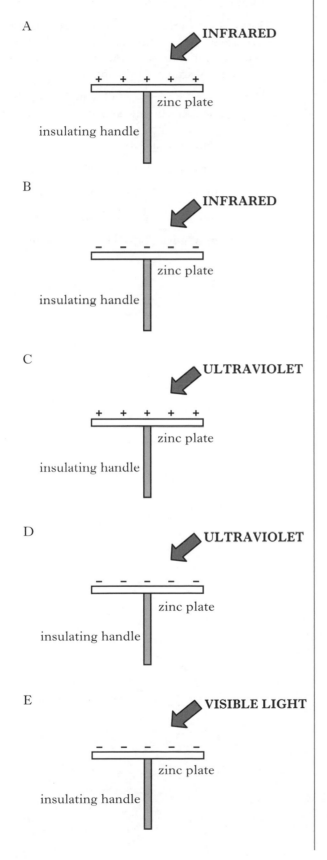

16. Electromagnetic radiation of frequency $9 \cdot 0 \times 10^{14}$ Hz is incident on a clean metal surface.

The work function of the metal is $5 \cdot 0 \times 10^{-19}$ J.

The maximum kinetic energy of a photoelectron released from the metal surface is

A $1 \cdot 0 \times 10^{-19}$ J

B $4 \cdot 0 \times 10^{-19}$ J

C $5 \cdot 0 \times 10^{-19}$ J

D $6 \cdot 0 \times 10^{-19}$ J

E $9 \cdot 0 \times 10^{-19}$ J.

17. In an atom, a photon of radiation is emitted when an electron makes a transition from a higher energy level to a lower energy level as shown.

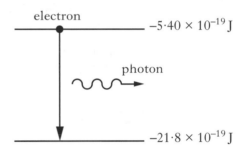

The wavelength of the radiation emitted due to an electron transition between the two energy levels shown is

A $1 \cdot 2 \times 10^{-7}$ m

B $7 \cdot 3 \times 10^{-8}$ m

C $8 \cdot 2 \times 10^{6}$ m

D $1 \cdot 4 \times 10^{7}$ m

E $2 \cdot 5 \times 10^{15}$ m.

[Turn over

18. Which of the following statements describes a spontaneous nuclear fission reaction?

A $^{235}_{92}\text{U} + ^{1}_{0}\text{n} \rightarrow ^{144}_{56}\text{Ba} + ^{90}_{36}\text{Kr} + 2\,^{1}_{0}\text{n}$

B $^{7}_{3}\text{Li} + ^{1}_{1}\text{H} \rightarrow ^{4}_{2}\text{He} + ^{4}_{2}\text{He}$

C $^{3}_{1}\text{H} + ^{2}_{1}\text{H} \rightarrow ^{4}_{2}\text{He} + ^{1}_{0}\text{n}$

D $^{226}_{88}\text{Ra} \rightarrow ^{222}_{86}\text{Rn} + ^{4}_{2}\text{He}$

E $^{216}_{84}\text{Po} \rightarrow ^{216}_{84}\text{Po} + \gamma$

19. The statement below represents a nuclear reaction.

$$^{3}_{1}\text{H} + ^{2}_{1}\text{H} \rightarrow ^{4}_{2}\text{He} + ^{1}_{0}\text{n}$$

The total mass on the left hand side is $8 \cdot 347 \times 10^{-27}\,\text{kg}$.

The total mass on the right hand side is $8 \cdot 316 \times 10^{-27}\,\text{kg}$.

The energy released during one nuclear reaction of this type is

A $9 \cdot 30 \times 10^{-21}\,\text{J}$

B $2 \cdot 79 \times 10^{-12}\,\text{J}$

C $7 \cdot 51 \times 10^{-10}\,\text{J}$

D $1 \cdot 50 \times 10^{-9}\,\text{J}$

E $2 \cdot 79 \times 10^{15}\,\text{J}$.

20. A source of gamma radiation is stored in a large container. A count rate of 160 counts per minute, after correction for background radiation, is recorded outside the container.

The container is to be shielded so that the corrected count rate at the same point outside the container is no more than 10 counts per minute.

Lead and water are available as shielding materials. For this source, the half-value thickness of lead is 11 mm and the half-value thickness of water is 110 mm.

Which of the following shielding arrangements meets the above requirements?

A   40 mm of lead only

B   33 mm of lead plus 110 mm of water

C   20 mm of lead plus 220 mm of water

D   11 mm of lead plus 275 mm of water

E   10 mm of lead plus 330 mm of water

SECTION B   *Marks*

Write your answers to questions 21 to 31 in the answer book.

21. Two cyclists choose different routes to travel from point **A** to a point **B** some distance away.

(a) Cyclist X travels 12 km due East (bearing 090). He then turns onto a bearing of 200 (20° West of South) and travels a further 15 km to arrive at **B**. He takes 1 hour 15 minutes to travel from **A** to **B**.

   (i) By scale drawing (or otherwise) find the displacement of **B** from **A**.   2

   (ii) Calculate the average velocity of cyclist X for the journey from **A** to **B**.   2

(b) Cyclist Y travels a total distance of 33 km by following a different route from **A** to **B** at an average speed of 22 km h^{-1}.

   (i) State the displacement of cyclist Y on completing this route.   1

   (ii) Calculate the average velocity of cyclist Y for the journey from **A** to **B**.   3

                                                               (8)

[Turn over

Marks

22. A golfer hits a ball from point **P**. The ball leaves the club with a velocity v at an angle of θ to the horizontal.

The ball travels through the air and lands at point **R**.

Midway between **P** and **R** there is a tree of height 10·0 m.

not to scale

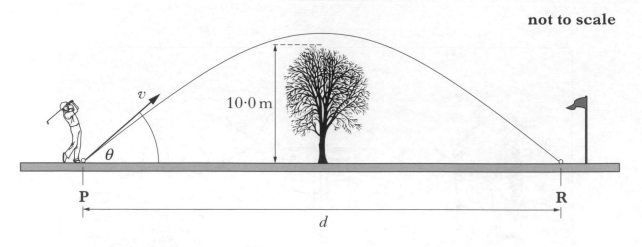

(a) The horizontal and vertical components of the ball's velocity during its flight are shown.

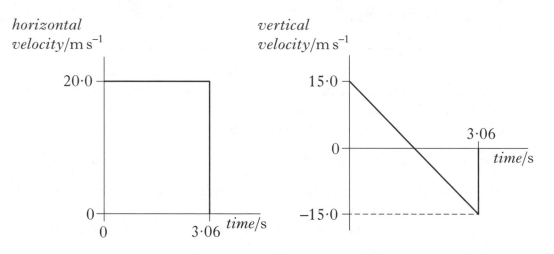

The effects of air resistance can be ignored.

Calculate:

   (i) the horizontal distance d;   **1**

   (ii) the maximum height of the ball above the ground.   **2**

(b) When the effects of air resistance are **not** ignored, the golf ball follows a different path.

Is the ball more or less likely to hit the tree?

You must justify your answer.   **2**

   (5)

Marks

23. An ion propulsion engine can be used to propel spacecraft to areas of deep space.

    A simplified diagram of a Xenon ion engine is shown.

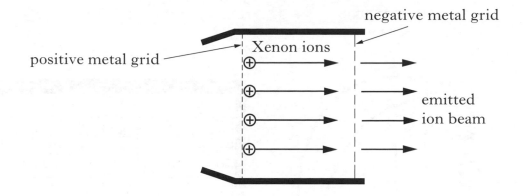

The Xenon ions are accelerated as they pass through an electric field between the charged metal grids. The emitted ion beam causes a force on the spacecraft in the opposite direction.

The spacecraft has a total mass of 750 kg.

The mass of a Xenon ion is $2 \cdot 18 \times 10^{-25}$ kg and its charge is $1 \cdot 60 \times 10^{-19}$ C. The potential difference between the charged metal grids is $1 \cdot 22$ kV.

(a) (i) Show that the work done on a Xenon ion as it moves through the electric field is $1 \cdot 95 \times 10^{-16}$ J.   **1**

    (ii) Assuming the ions are accelerated from rest, calculate the speed of a Xenon ion as it leaves the engine.   **2**

(b) The ion beam exerts a constant force of $0 \cdot 070$ N on the spacecraft. Calculate the change in speed of the spacecraft during a 60 second period of time.   **2**

(c) A different ion propulsion engine uses Krypton ions which have a smaller mass than Xenon ions. The Krypton engine emits the same number of ions per second at the same speed as the Xenon engine.

Which of the two engines produces a greater force?

Justify your answer.   **2**

(7)

[Turn over

Marks

24. A student carries out an experiment to investigate the relationship between the pressure and temperature of a fixed mass of gas. The apparatus used is shown.

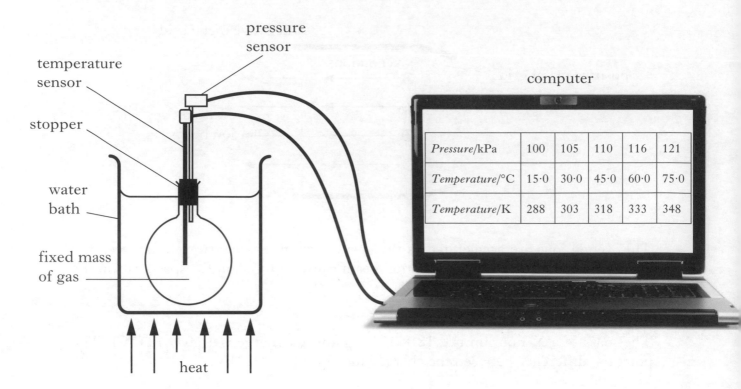

The pressure and temperature of the gas are recorded using sensors connected to a computer. The gas is heated slowly in the water bath and a series of readings is taken.

The volume of the gas remains constant during the experiment.

The results are shown.

Pressure/kPa	100	105	110	116	121
Temperature/°C	15·0	30·0	45·0	60·0	75·0
Temperature/K	288	303	318	333	348

(a) Using **all** the relevant data, establish the relationship between the pressure and the temperature of the gas.   2

(b) Use the kinetic model to explain the change in pressure as the temperature of the gas increases.   2

(c) Explain why the level of water in the water bath should be above the bottom of the stopper.   1

                                                                                                (5)

Marks

25. A student carries out two experiments using different power supplies connected to a lamp of resistance 6·0 Ω.

    (a) In the first experiment the lamp is connected to a power supply of e.m.f. 12 V and internal resistance 2·0 Ω as shown.

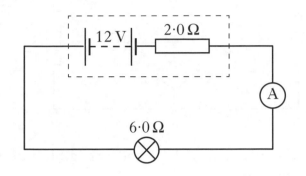

    Calculate:

        (i) the reading on the ammeter;   2

        (ii) the lost volts;   1

        (iii) the output power of the lamp.   2

    (b) In the second experiment the lamp is connected to a different power supply. This supply has the same e.m.f. as the supply in part (a) but a different value of internal resistance.

    The output power of the lamp is now greater.

    Assuming the resistance of the lamp has not changed, is the internal resistance of the new power supply less than, equal to, or greater than the internal resistance of the original supply?

    Justify your answer.   2

        (7)

[Turn over

Marks

26. The charging and discharging of a capacitor are investigated using the circuit shown.

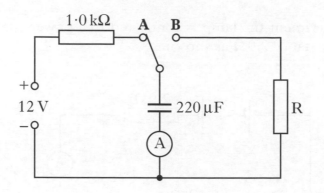

The power supply has an e.m.f. of 12 V and negligible internal resistance. The capacitor is initially uncharged.

(a) The switch is connected to **A** and the capacitor starts to charge. Sketch a graph showing how the voltage across the plates of the capacitor varies with time. Your graph should start from the moment the switch is connected to **A** until the capacitor is fully charged.

Numerical values are only required on the voltage axis.   **2**

(b) The capacitor is now discharged by moving the switch to **B**.

The graph of current against time as the capacitor discharges is shown.

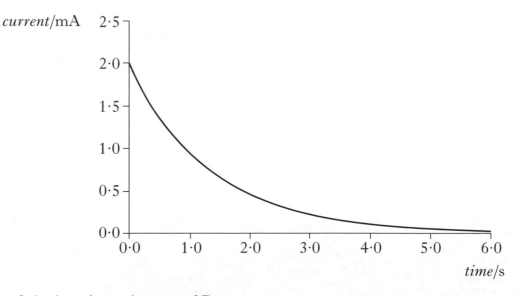

Calculate the resistance of R.   **2**

26. (continued)   *Marks*

(c) The 220 μF capacitor is now replaced with one of different value. This new capacitor is fully charged by moving the switch to **A**. It is then discharged by moving the switch to **B**.

The graph of current against time as this capacitor discharges is shown.

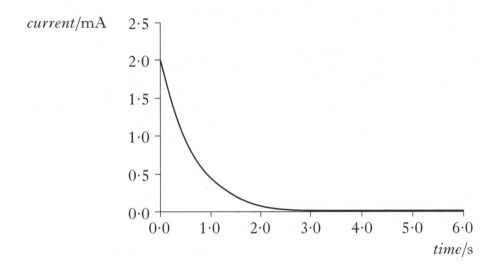

(i) Explain why the value of the initial discharging current remains the same as in part (*b*).   1

(ii) How does the capacitance of this capacitor compare with the capacitance of the original 220 μF capacitor?

You must justify your answer.   2

                                                                                        (7)

[Turn over

[BLANK PAGE]

Marks

27. A fabric has been developed for use as a sensor in a breathing rate monitor. The graph shows how the resistance of a 50 mm length of this fabric changes as it is stretched.

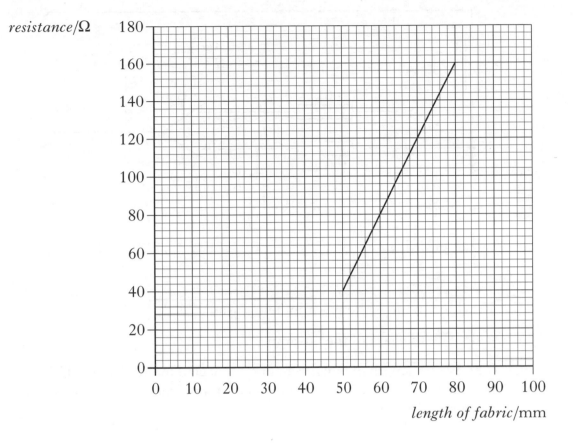

A sample of the fabric of unstretched length 50 mm is connected in a Wheatstone bridge circuit.

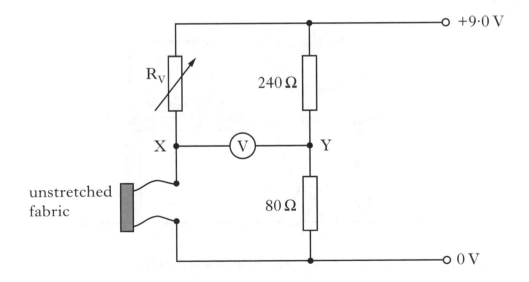

(a) The variable resistor R_V is adjusted until the bridge is balanced.

Show that the resistance of R_V is now 120 Ω.

2

27. (continued)   *Marks*

(b) The Wheatstone bridge is now connected to an op-amp circuit as shown.

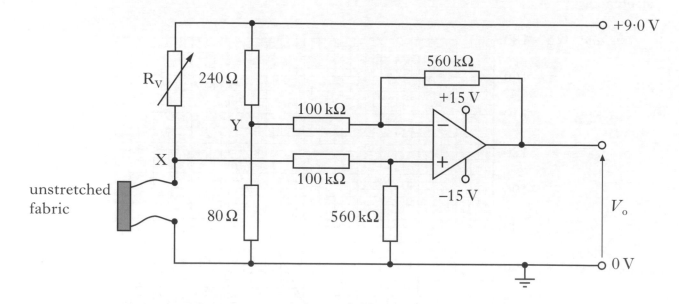

(i)   In which mode is the op-amp being used?   **1**

(ii) Calculate the gain of the op-amp.   **1**

(iii) The 50 mm length of fabric remains connected in the circuit. This sensor is
      attached to a patient to monitor his chest movements. The fabric stretches
      as he breathes in.

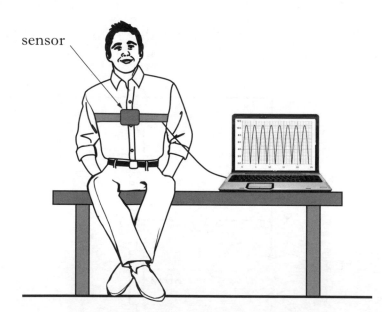

The potential at Y is 2·25 V. R_V remains at 120 Ω.

The output from the op-amp is connected to a computer.

The voltage V_o produced as the patient breathes in and out for 24 seconds
is shown.

27. *(b)* **(iii) (continued)**   *Marks*

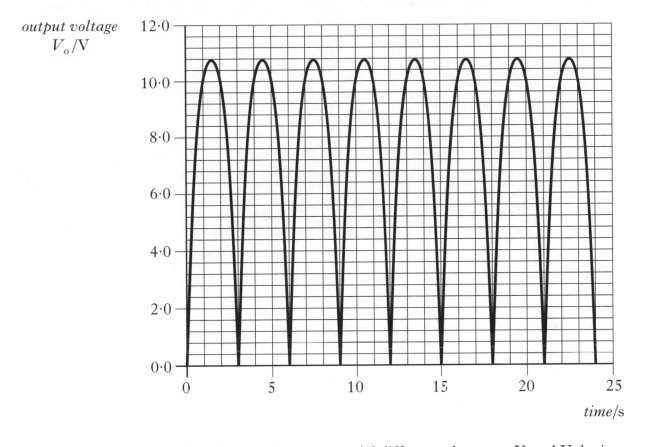

output voltage V_o/V

(A) Calculate the maximum potential difference between X and Y during this time.   **2**

(B) Calculate the maximum length of the fabric during this time.   **3**

(9)

[Turn over

Marks

28. A technician investigates the path of laser light as it passes through a glass tank filled with water. The light enters the glass tank along the normal at **C** then reflects off a mirror submerged in the water.

not to scale

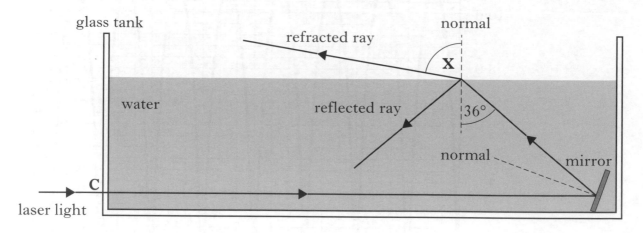

The refractive index of water for this laser light is 1·33.

(a) Calculate angle **X**.   2

(b) The mirror is now adjusted until the light follows the paths shown.

not to scale

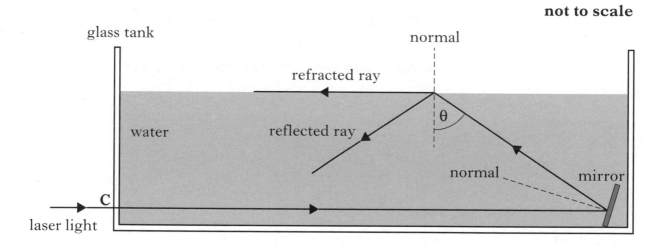

   (i) State why the value of θ is equal to the critical angle for this laser light in water.   1

   (ii) Calculate angle θ.   2

(c) The water is now replaced with a liquid which has a greater refractive index. The mirror is kept at the same angle as in part (b) and the incident ray again enters the tank along the normal at **C**.

Draw a sketch which shows the path of the light ray after it has reflected off the mirror.

Your sketch should only show what happens at the surface of the liquid.   1

   (6)

Marks

29. A manufacturer claims that a grating consists of $3 \cdot 00 \times 10^5$ lines per metre and is accurate to $\pm\, 2 \cdot 0\%$. A technician decides to test this claim. She directs laser light of wavelength 633 nm onto the grating.

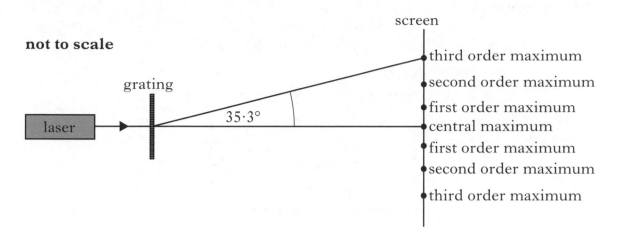

She measures the angle between the central maximum and the third order maximum to be $35 \cdot 3°$.

(*a*) Calculate the value she obtains for the slit separation for this grating.　　　　**2**

(*b*) What value does she determine for the number of lines per metre for this grating?　　**1**

(*c*) Does the technician's value for the number of lines per metre agree with the manufacturer's claim of $3 \cdot 00 \times 10^5$ lines per metre $\pm\, 2 \cdot 0\%$?

You must justify your answer by calculation.　　　　**2**

(5)

[Turn over

Marks

30. (*a*) An n-type semiconductor is formed by adding impurity atoms to a sample of pure semiconductor material.

State the effect that the addition of the impurity atoms has on the resistance of the material.   **1**

(*b*) A p-n junction is used as a photodiode as shown.

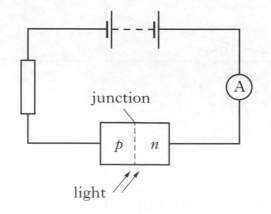

(i) In which mode is the photodiode operating?   **1**

(ii) The irradiance of the light on the junction of the photodiode is now increased.

Explain what happens to the current in the circuit.   **2**

(*c*) The photodiode is placed at a distance of 1·2 m from a small lamp. The reading on the ammeter is 3·0 μA.

The photodiode is now moved to a distance of 0·80 m from the same lamp. Calculate the new reading on the ammeter.   **2**

    (6)

Marks

31. A medical physicist is investigating the effects of radiation on tissue samples.

One sample of tissue receives an absorbed dose of $500\,\mu Gy$ of radiation from a source.

The radiation weighting factors of different types of radiation are shown.

Type of radiation	Radiation weighting factor (w_R)
gamma	1
thermal neutrons	3
fast neutrons	10
alpha	20

(a) The tissue sample has a mass of $0\cdot040\,kg$. Calculate the total energy absorbed by the tissue.　　2

(b) The average equivalent dose rate for this tissue sample is $5\cdot00\,mSv\,h^{-1}$.
The tissue is exposed to radiation for 2 hours.

Which type of radiation is the medical physicist using?

Justify your answer by calculation.　　3

(5)

[END OF QUESTION PAPER]

[BLANK PAGE]

[BLANK PAGE]

X069/12/02

NATIONAL QUALIFICATIONS 2013	MONDAY, 27 MAY 1.00 PM – 3.30 PM	PHYSICS HIGHER

Read Carefully

Reference may be made to the Physics Data Booklet.

1 All questions should be attempted.

Section A (questions 1 to 20)

2 Check that the answer sheet is for Physics Higher (Section A).

3 For this section of the examination you must use an **HB pencil** and, where necessary, an eraser.

4 Check that the answer sheet you have been given has **your name**, **date of birth**, **SCN** (Scottish Candidate Number) and **Centre Name** printed on it.

Do not change any of these details.

5 If any of this information is wrong, tell the Invigilator immediately.

6 If this information is correct, **print** your name and seat number in the boxes provided.

7 There is **only one correct** answer to each question.

8 Any rough working should be done on the question paper or the rough working sheet, **not** on your answer sheet.

9 At the end of the exam, put the **answer sheet for Section A inside the front cover of your answer book**.

10 Instructions as to how to record your answers to questions 1–20 are given on page three.

Section B (questions 21 to 31)

11 Answer the questions numbered 21 to 31 in the answer book provided.

12 **All answers must be written clearly and legibly in ink**.

13 Fill in the details on the front of the answer book.

14 Enter the question number clearly in the margin of the answer book beside each of your answers to questions 21 to 31.

15 Care should be taken to give an appropriate number of significant figures in the final answers to calculations.

16 Where additional paper, eg square ruled paper, is used, write your name and SCN (Scottish Candidate Number) on it and place it inside the front cover of your answer booklet.

DATA SHEET
COMMON PHYSICAL QUANTITIES

Quantity	Symbol	Value	Quantity	Symbol	Value
Speed of light in vacuum	c	$3 \cdot 00 \times 10^8 \, \mathrm{m\,s^{-1}}$	Mass of electron	m_e	$9 \cdot 11 \times 10^{-31} \, \mathrm{kg}$
Magnitude of the charge on an electron	e	$1 \cdot 60 \times 10^{-19} \, \mathrm{C}$	Mass of neutron	m_n	$1 \cdot 675 \times 10^{-27} \, \mathrm{kg}$
Gravitational acceleration on Earth	g	$9 \cdot 8 \, \mathrm{m\,s^{-2}}$	Mass of proton	m_p	$1 \cdot 673 \times 10^{-27} \, \mathrm{kg}$
Planck's constant	h	$6 \cdot 63 \times 10^{-34} \, \mathrm{J\,s}$			

REFRACTIVE INDICES
The refractive indices refer to sodium light of wavelength 589 nm and to substances at a temperature of 273 K.

Substance	Refractive index	Substance	Refractive index
Diamond	2·42	Water	1·33
Crown glass	1·50	Air	1·00

SPECTRAL LINES

Element	Wavelength/nm	Colour	Element	Wavelength/nm	Colour
Hydrogen	656	Red	Cadmium	644	Red
	486	Blue-green		509	Green
	434	Blue-violet		480	Blue
	410	Violet		*Lasers*	
	397	Ultraviolet	Element	Wavelength/nm	Colour
	389	Ultraviolet	Carbon dioxide	9550 } 10590 }	Infrared
Sodium	589	Yellow	Helium-neon	633	Red

PROPERTIES OF SELECTED MATERIALS

Substance	Density/kg m^{-3}	Melting Point/K	Boiling Point/K
Aluminium	$2 \cdot 70 \times 10^3$	933	2623
Copper	$8 \cdot 96 \times 10^3$	1357	2853
Ice	$9 \cdot 20 \times 10^2$	273	. . . .
Sea Water	$1 \cdot 02 \times 10^3$	264	377
Water	$1 \cdot 00 \times 10^3$	273	373
Air	$1 \cdot 29$	. . . .	. . . .
Hydrogen	$9 \cdot 0 \times 10^{-2}$	14	20

The gas densities refer to a temperature of 273 K and a pressure of $1 \cdot 01 \times 10^5 \, \mathrm{Pa}$.

SECTION A

For questions 1 to 20 in this section of the paper the answer to each question is either A, B, C, D or E. Decide what your answer is, then, using your pencil, put a horizontal line in the space provided—see the example below.

EXAMPLE

The energy unit measured by the electricity meter in your home is the

A kilowatt-hour

B ampere

C watt

D coulomb

E volt.

The correct answer is **A**—kilowatt-hour. The answer **A** has been clearly marked in **pencil** with a horizontal line (see below).

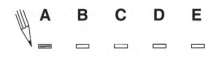

Changing an answer

If you decide to change your answer, carefully erase your first answer and, using your pencil, fill in the answer you want. The answer below has been changed to **E**.

[Turn over

SECTION A

Answer questions 1–20 on the answer sheet.

1. Which of the following is a vector quantity?

   A   distance

   B   time

   C   speed

   D   energy

   E   weight

2. An object starts from rest and accelerates in a straight line.

   The graph shows how the acceleration of the object varies with time.

   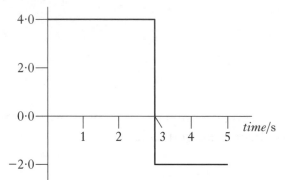

   The speed of the object at 5 seconds is

   A $2\,\mathrm{m\,s^{-1}}$

   B $8\,\mathrm{m\,s^{-1}}$

   C $12\,\mathrm{m\,s^{-1}}$

   D $16\,\mathrm{m\,s^{-1}}$

   E $20\,\mathrm{m\,s^{-1}}$.

3. A vehicle runs down a slope as shown.

   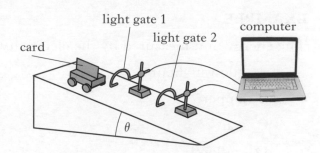

   The following results are obtained.

   angle of slope,
   $$\theta = 15 \cdot 0 \pm 0 \cdot 5°$$

   length of card on top of vehicle,
   $$d = 0 \cdot 020 \pm 0 \cdot 001\,\mathrm{m}$$

   time for card to pass light gate 1,
   $$t_1 = 0 \cdot 40 \pm 0 \cdot 01\,\mathrm{s}$$

   time for card to pass light gate 2,
   $$t_2 = 0 \cdot 25 \pm 0 \cdot 01\,\mathrm{s}$$

   time for vehicle to travel between the light gates,
   $$t_3 = 0 \cdot 50 \pm 0 \cdot 01\,\mathrm{s}$$

   Which quantity has the largest percentage uncertainty?

   A θ

   B d

   C t_1

   D t_2

   E t_3

4. Two blocks are linked by a newton balance of negligible mass.

   The blocks are placed on a level, frictionless surface. A force of $18 \cdot 0\,\mathrm{N}$ is applied to the blocks as shown.

   The reading on the newton balance is

   A $7 \cdot 2\,\mathrm{N}$

   B $9 \cdot 0\,\mathrm{N}$

   C $10 \cdot 8\,\mathrm{N}$

   D $18 \cdot 0\,\mathrm{N}$

   E $40 \cdot 0\,\mathrm{N}$.

5. A box is suspended by a rope under the surface of the sea.

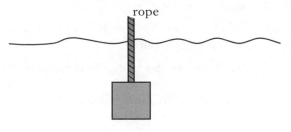

Which diagram shows the vertical forces acting on the box?

A

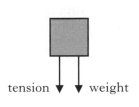

B

tension ↓   ↓ weight

C   tension ↑   ↑ upthrust

weight ↓

D   upthrust ↑

tension ↓   ↓ weight

E   tension ↑   ↑ upthrust

gravity ↓   ↓ weight

6. A cannon of mass 2.0×10^3 kg fires a cannonball of mass 5.00 kg.

The cannonball leaves the cannon with a speed of $50.0 \, \text{m s}^{-1}$.

The speed of the cannon immediately after firing is

A $0.125 \, \text{m s}^{-1}$

B $8.00 \, \text{m s}^{-1}$

C $39.9 \, \text{m s}^{-1}$

D $40.1 \, \text{m s}^{-1}$

E $200 \, \text{m s}^{-1}$.

7. The pressure of a gas in a sealed syringe is 1.5×10^5 Pa.

The temperature of the gas is 27 °C.

The temperature of the gas is now raised by 10 °C and the volume of the gas halved.

The new pressure of the gas in the syringe is

A 1.1×10^5 Pa

B 2.8×10^5 Pa

C 3.1×10^5 Pa

D 4.1×10^5 Pa

E 11×10^5 Pa.

8. A student writes the following statements about electric fields.

I   There is a force on a charge in an electric field.

II   When an electric field is applied to a conductor, the free electric charges in the conductor move.

III   Work is done when a charge is moved in an electric field.

Which of the statements is/are correct?

A   I only

B   II only

C   I and II only

D   I and III only

E   I, II and III

[Turn over

9. The diagram shows a Wheatstone bridge.

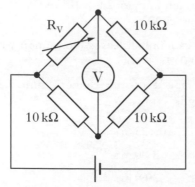

The reading on the voltmeter is zero.

The variable resistor R_V is now altered in steps of $1\,\Omega$ and each corresponding reading on the voltmeter is noted.

Which of the following graphs shows how the reading on the voltmeter, V, varies with the change in resistance ΔR?

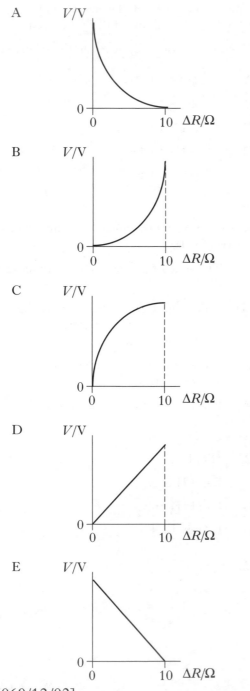

10. The capacitance of a capacitor is $1000\,\mu F$. The potential difference (p.d.) across the capacitor is $100\,V$. The charge stored by the capacitor is $0.10\,C$.

The charge on the capacitor is now reduced to half its original value.

Which row in the table shows the capacitance of the capacitor and the p.d. across the capacitor, for this new value of charge?

	Capacitance/μF	p.d./V
A	1000	200
B	500	100
C	1000	100
D	500	50
E	1000	50

11. The graph shows how the charge, Q, stored on a capacitor varies with the potential difference, V, across the capacitor.

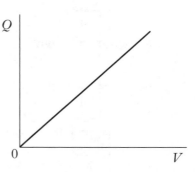

Which of the following statements is/are correct?

  I The gradient of the graph represents the capacitance of the capacitor.

  II The area under the graph represents the work done in charging the capacitor.

  III The energy, E, stored in the capacitor is given by the equation $E = QV$.

A   I only

B   II only

C   III only

D   I and II only

E   I, II and III

12. The following circuit shows a constant voltage a.c. supply connected to a resistor and capacitor in parallel.

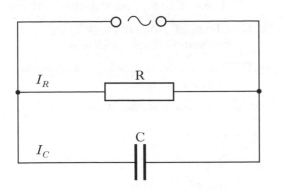

Which pair of graphs shows how the r.m.s. currents I_R and I_C vary as the frequency, f, of the supply is increased?

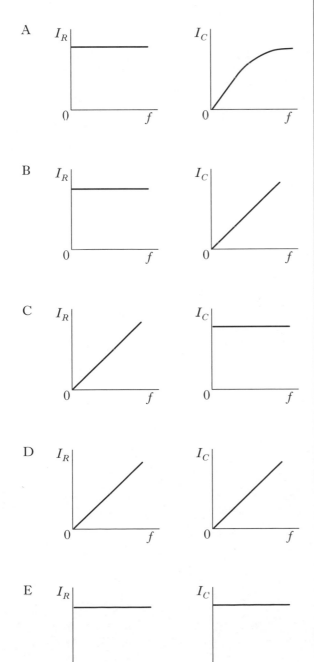

13. A physicist designs the amplifier circuit shown.

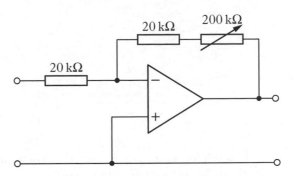

In this circuit, adjustment of the resistance of the variable resistor from zero to $200\,k\Omega$ allows the voltage gain to be altered over the range

A   zero to one

B   zero to ten

C   zero to eleven

D   one to ten

E   one to eleven.

14. The energy of a water wave depends on its

A   amplitude

B   period

C   phase

D   speed

E   wavelength.

15. Light travels from air into glass.

Which row in the table describes what happens to the speed, frequency and wavelength of the light?

	Speed	Frequency	Wavelength
A	increases	decreases	stays constant
B	decreases	stays constant	decreases
C	stays constant	decreases	decreases
D	increases	stays constant	increases
E	decreases	decreases	stays constant

16. The irradiance of light can be measured in

    A   W

    B $W\,m^{-1}$

    C $W\,m$

    D $W\,m^{-2}$

    E $W\,m^2$.

17. Ultraviolet radiation causes the emission of photoelectrons from a zinc plate.

    The irradiance of the ultraviolet radiation on the zinc plate is increased.

    Which row in the table shows the effect of this change?

	Maximum kinetic energy of a photoelectron	*Number of photoelectrons emitted per second*
A	increases	no change
B	no change	increases
C	no change	no change
D	increases	increases
E	decreases	increases

18. A student reads the following passage in a physics dictionary.

    "*. . . is a solid state device in which positive and negative charge carriers are produced by the action of light on a p-n junction.*"

    The passage describes

    A   a thermistor

    B   a MOSFET

    C   a photodiode

    D   a laser

    E   an LED.

19. A student makes the following statements about Rutherford's model of the atom.

    I   The nucleus has a relatively small diameter compared with that of the atom.

    II Most of the mass of the atom is concentrated in the nucleus.

    III The nucleus consists of positive and negative charges.

    Which of these statements is/are correct?

    A   I only

    B   II only

    C   III only

    D   I and II only

    E   I, II and III

20. Part of a radioactive decay series is shown in the diagram.

The symbols X_1 to X_5 represent nuclides in this series.

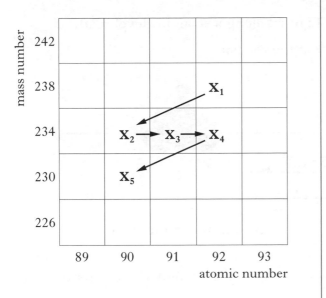

A student makes the following statements about the decay series.

   I   Nuclides X_2 and X_3 contain the same number of protons.

  II Nuclide X_1 decays into nuclide X_2 by emitting an alpha particle.

III Nuclide X_3 decays into nuclide X_4 by emitting a beta particle.

Which of these statements is/are correct?

A   I only

B   II only

C   III only

D   II and III only

E   I, II and III

[Turn over

SECTION B

Marks

Write your answers to questions 21 to 31 in the answer book.

21. A car is travelling at a constant speed of $15\,\mathrm{m\,s^{-1}}$ along a straight, level road.

It passes a motorcycle which is stationary at the roadside.

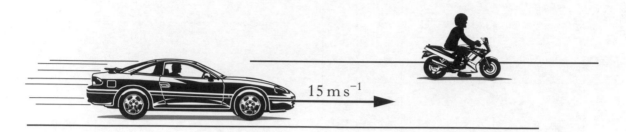

$15\,\mathrm{m\,s^{-1}}$

At the instant the car passes, the motorcycle starts to move in the same direction as the car.

The graph shows the motion of each vehicle from the instant the car passes the motorcycle.

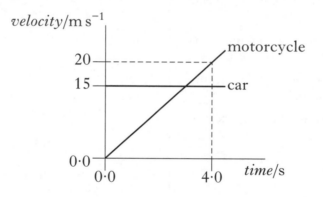

(a) Show that the initial acceleration of the motorcycle is $5{\cdot}0\,\mathrm{m\,s^{-2}}$.

1

(b) Calculate the distance between the car and the motorcycle at $4{\cdot}0\,\mathrm{s}$.

2

(c) The total mass of the motorcycle and rider is $290\,\mathrm{kg}$. At a time of $2{\cdot}0\,\mathrm{s}$ the driving force on the motorcycle is $1800\,\mathrm{N}$.

   (i) Calculate the frictional force acting on the motorcycle at this time.

2

   (ii) Explain why the driving force must be increased with time to maintain a constant acceleration.

1

(6)

Marks

22. A tennis player strikes a ball at a height of 2·5 m above the ground.

    The ball leaves the racquet travelling horizontally at 24 m s⁻¹.

    It travels through the air and hits the ground at point **X** on the other side of the net.

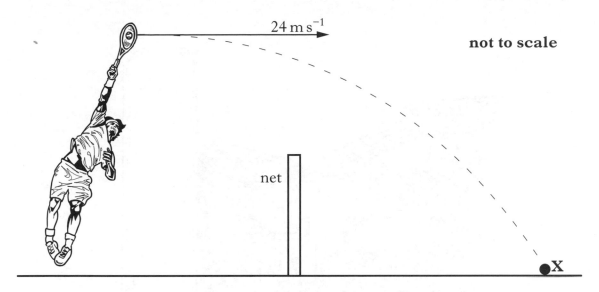

The effects of air resistance can be ignored.

(a) The ball takes 0·50 s to travel to the net.

   Calculate the height of the ball above the ground at this time.   2

(b) By scale drawing, or otherwise, calculate the velocity of the ball as it hits the ground at **X**.   3

(c) After playing with the same ball for a time, the temperature of the gas inside the ball increases.

   Using the kinetic model, describe how this increase in temperature affects the pressure of the gas in the ball. Assume that the mass of gas and the volume of the ball remain constant.   2

   (7)

[Turn over

Marks

23. The force applied by a seat belt on a crash test dummy is being investigated. The crash test dummy is placed in a car.

    The car then travels along a test track at a speed of $13 \cdot 4 \, \text{m s}^{-1}$, collides with a wall and comes to rest.

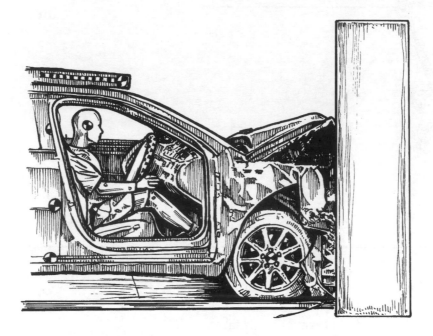

(a) State the law of conservation of linear momentum.   1

(b) The total mass of the car and dummy is 1200 kg.

    Calculate the change in momentum of the car and dummy in the collision.   2

(c) The crash test dummy has a mass of 75 kg and is wearing a seat belt.

    During the collision the dummy travels a distance of 0·48 m while coming to rest.

    Calculate the average force exerted on the dummy by the seat belt.   3

          (6)

24. A diver is measuring the pressure at different depths in the sea using a simple pressure gauge. Part of the pressure gauge consists of a cylinder containing gas trapped by a moveable piston.

Marks

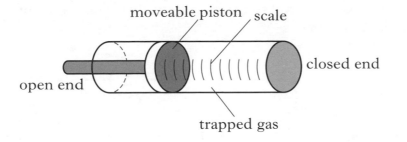

At sea level, the atmospheric pressure is $1{\cdot}01 \times 10^5$ Pa and the trapped gas exerts a force of 262 N on the piston.

(a) Calculate the area of the piston.

2

(b) The diver now descends to a depth, h, where the gauge registers a total pressure of $5{\cdot}13 \times 10^5$ Pa.

The density of the sea water is $1{\cdot}02 \times 10^3 \, \text{kg m}^{-3}$.

The temperature of the trapped gas remains constant.

  (i) Calculate this depth, h.

3

  (ii) While at this depth, a bubble of gas is released from the diver's breathing apparatus.

  State what happens to the volume of this bubble as it rises to the surface. Justify your answer.

1

(c) The pressure gauge is now used as the sensor in the circuit shown to indicate the depth of a mini-submarine. A variable resistor, R_V, is attached to the moveable piston of the pressure gauge.

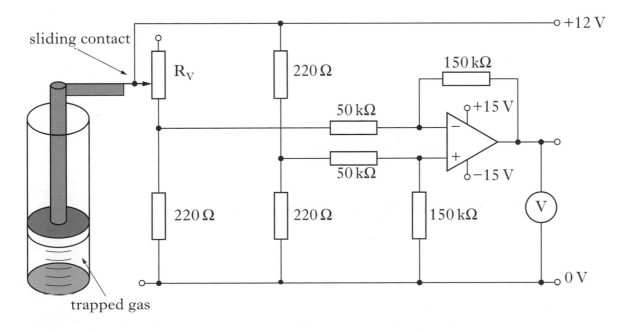

The resistance of R_V decreases as the depth of the mini-submarine increases.

Calculate the reading on the voltmeter when the value of R_V is zero.

3

Marks

25. A thermocouple is a device that produces an e.m.f. when heated.

(*a*) A technician uses the circuit shown to investigate the operation of a thermocouple when heated in a flame.

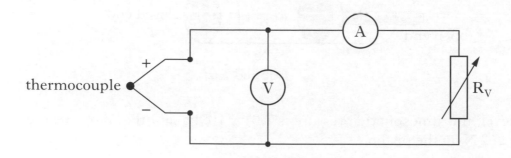

Readings of current and potential difference (p.d.) are recorded for different settings of the variable resistor R_V.

The graph of p.d. against current is shown.

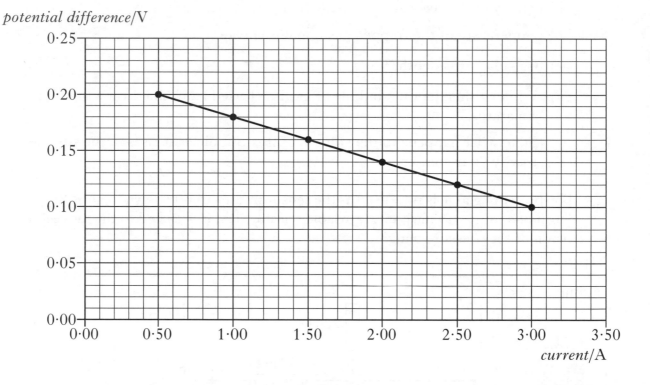

Use information from the graph to find:

   (i) the e.m.f. produced by the thermocouple;   **1**

  (ii) the internal resistance of the thermocouple.   **2**

25. (continued)

Marks

(b) A **different** thermocouple is to be used as part of a safety device in a gas oven. The safety device turns off the gas supply to the oven if the flame goes out. The thermocouple is connected to a coil of resistance $0.12\,\Omega$ which operates a magnetic gas valve.

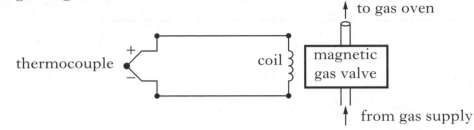

When the current in the coil is less than $2.5\,A$, the gas valve is closed.

The temperature of the flame in the gas oven is $800\,°C$.

The manufacturer's data for this thermocouple is shown in the two graphs.

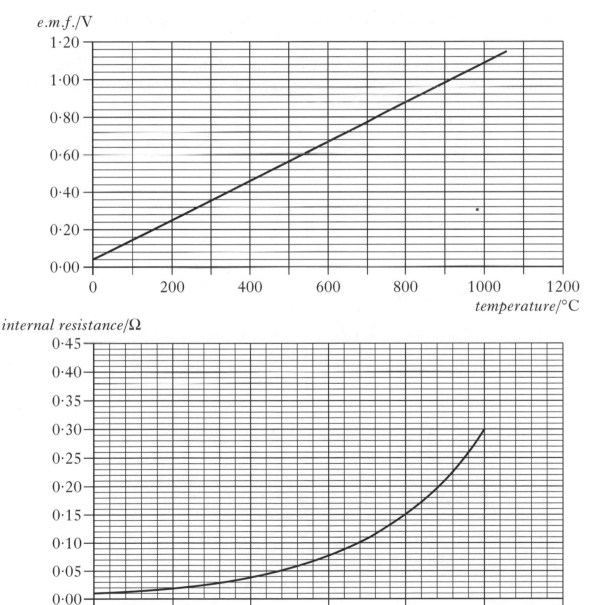

Is this thermocouple suitable as a source of e.m.f. for the gas valve to be open at a temperature of $800\,°C$?

You must justify your answer.

3

Marks

26. The circuit shown is used to compare the voltage from a battery and the voltage produced by a signal generator.

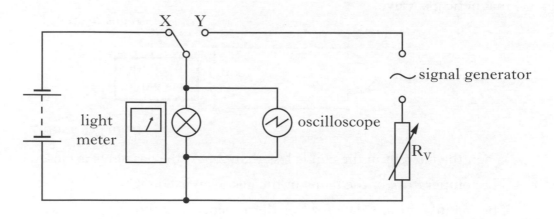

The switch is connected to X and the voltage across the lamp is 2·30 V. The reading on the light meter is recorded.

The switch is now connected to Y. The resistance of R_V is adjusted until the light meter reading is the same as before. The trace on the oscilloscope screen is shown.

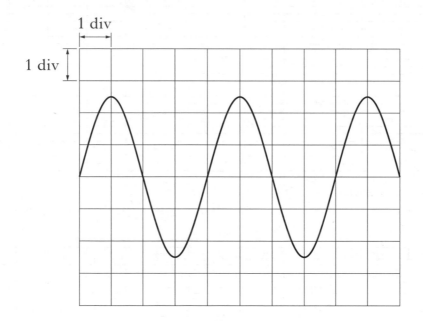

(a) The timebase setting is 0·01 s/div.

Calculate the frequency of the output voltage of the signal generator.   2

(b) Calculate the peak value of the voltage displayed on the oscilloscope.   2

(c) With the switch still connected to Y, the signal generator frequency is now doubled without altering the output voltage.

State what happens to the reading on the light meter.

Justify your answer.   1

(5)

Marks

27. Part of a camera flash circuit operates at 250 V d.c. The circuit includes a 15·0 kΩ resistor and a 470 μF capacitor. The capacitor is initially uncharged.

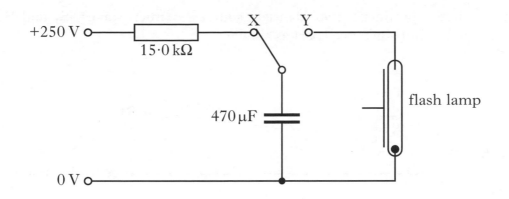

(a) The capacitor is now charged by connecting the switch to X.

   (i) Calculate the initial charging current.   2

   (ii) Sketch a graph to show how the voltage across the capacitor varies with time from the moment the switch is connected to X. Numerical values are required on the voltage axis.   1

   (iii) Show that the energy stored in the capacitor is 14·7 J when it is fully charged.   1

(b) When a flash photograph is taken, the switch is connected to Y and the capacitor discharges through the flash lamp in a time of 200 μs.

   Calculate the average power output of the flash lamp.   2

(c) The flash cannot be fired again for another photograph until the capacitor has recharged. The time for this to happen is called the recycle time.

   How could the circuit be modified to reduce the recycle time without altering the power output of the flash?   1

   (7)

[Turn over

Marks

28. A student is using different types of electromagnetic radiation to investigate interference.

    (a) In the first experiment, two identical sources of microwaves, S_1 and S_2, are positioned a short distance apart as shown.

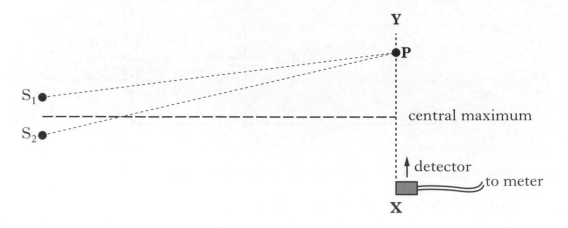

    (i) The student moves a microwave detector from X towards Y. The reading on the meter increases and decreases regularly.

    Explain, in terms of waves, what causes the minimum readings to occur.   **1**

    (ii) The **third** maximum from the central maximum is located at P.

    The distance from S_1 to P is 620 mm.

    The wavelength of the waves is 28 mm.

    Calculate the distance from S_2 to P.   **2**

    (b) In the second experiment, a beam of parallel, monochromatic light is incident on a grating. An interference pattern is produced on a screen. The edges of the screen are at an angle of 40° to the centre of the grating as shown.

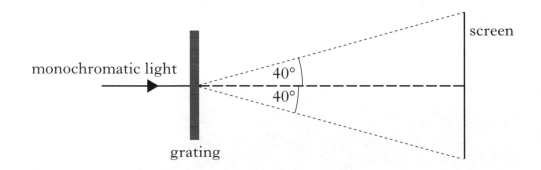

    The wavelength of the light is 420 nm and the separation of the slits on the grating is $3 \cdot 27 \times 10^{-6}$ m.

    Determine the total number of maxima visible on the screen.   **3**

       (6)

Marks

29. A student places a glass paperweight containing air bubbles on a sheet of white paper.

The student notices that when white light passes through the paperweight, a pattern of spectra is produced.

The student decides to study this effect in more detail by carrying out an experiment in the laboratory.

A ray of green light follows the path shown as it enters an air bubble inside glass.

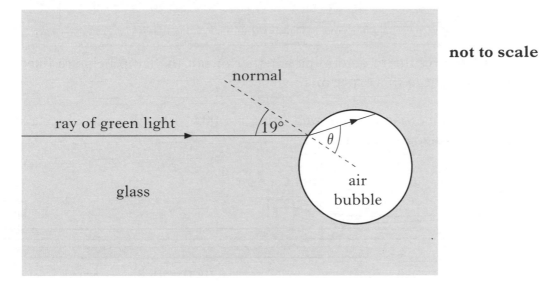

not to scale

The refractive index of the glass for this light is 1·49.

(a) Calculate the angle of refraction, θ, inside the air bubble.   2

(b) Calculate the maximum angle of incidence at which a ray of green light can enter the air bubble.   2

(c) The student now replaces the ray of green light with a ray of white light.

Explain why a spectrum is produced.   1

(5)

[Turn over

Marks

30. (*a*) A technician uses the following apparatus to investigate the relationship between the irradiance of the light from a lamp and the distance from it.

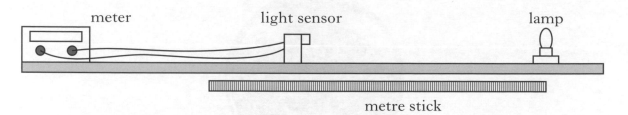

The results of the experiment are shown.

Distance between light sensor and lamp/m	Irradiance/units
0·10	242
0·15	106
0·20	60
0·25	39

Use **all** the results to determine whether or not the lamp behaves like a point source of light in this experiment.

2

(*b*) The experiment is now repeated using a $1·00 \times 10^{-4}$ W laser which produces light of wavelength 633 nm.

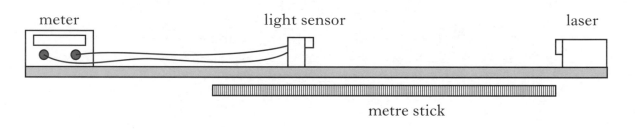

(i) Explain why the results obtained with the laser differ from those obtained using the lamp.

1

(ii) Calculate the number of photons emitted by the laser each second.

3

(iii) Light from the laser is described as *coherent*.

Describe, in terms of photons, two differences between the light from the laser and the light from the lamp used in part (*a*).

1

(7)

Marks

31. (*a*) The following statement represents a nuclear reaction.

$$^{A}_{Z}\text{X} + {}^{2}_{1}\text{H} \longrightarrow 2\,^{4}_{2}\text{He} + {}^{1}_{0}\text{n} + \text{energy}$$

The masses of some of the particles involved in this reaction are shown in the table.

Particle	Mass/kg
$^{2}_{1}\text{H}$	$3 \cdot 342 \times 10^{-27}$
$^{4}_{2}\text{He}$	$6 \cdot 642 \times 10^{-27}$
$^{1}_{0}\text{n}$	$1 \cdot 675 \times 10^{-27}$

(i) Use the data booklet to identify the element **X**. 1

(ii) The energy released in this reaction is $2 \cdot 97 \times 10^{-12}$ J.

Calculate the mass of the nucleus $^{A}_{Z}\text{X}$. 3

(*b*) The crew of an aircraft receives an absorbed dose at a rate of $2 \cdot 0\,\mu\text{Gy h}^{-1}$ of gamma rays, $1 \cdot 25\,\mu\text{Gy h}^{-1}$ from protons and $0 \cdot 20\,\mu\text{Gy h}^{-1}$ from fast neutrons.

The table shows the radiation weighting factor for various types of radiation.

Type	Radiation weighting factor
gamma rays	1
protons	2
thermal neutrons	5
fast neutrons	10
alpha particles	20

Calculate the equivalent dose received by a member of the crew during a 12 hour flight. 2

(6)

[END OF QUESTION PAPER]

SQA HIGHER PHYSICS
2009–2013

PHYSICS HIGHER
2009

SECTION A

1. B	2. C	3. B	4. D
5. C	6. A	7. C	8. D
9. C	10. B	11. C	12. A
13. C	14. D	15. E	16. B
17. D	18. E	19. A	20. E

SECTION B

21. (a) (i) $u_h = 6 \cdot 5 \cos 50° = 4 \cdot 2 \text{ m s}^{-1}$

 (ii) $u_v = 6 \cdot 5 \sin 50° = 5 \cdot 0 \text{ m s}^{-1}$

 (b) $t = \dfrac{s}{v}$

 $= \dfrac{2 \cdot 9}{4 \cdot 2}$

 $= 0 \cdot 69 \text{ (s)}$

 (c) $s = ut + \frac{1}{2} at^2$

 $= 5 \times 0 \cdot 69 + \frac{1}{2} \times -9 \cdot 8 \times (0 \cdot 69)^2$

 $= 1 \cdot 1 \text{ (m)}$

 so height $\boldsymbol{h} = 2 \cdot 3 + 1 \cdot 1 = 3 \cdot 4 \text{ m}$

 (d) Ball would **not** land in basket

 (initial) vertical speed would increase

 So ball is higher than the basket when it has travelled 2·9 m horizontally

 or

 So ball has travelled further horizontally when it is at the same height as the basket

22. (a) (i) (A)

 $\text{mean} = \dfrac{248 + 259 + 251 + 263 + 254}{5}$

 $= 255 \text{ μs}$

 (B) uncertainty $= \dfrac{263 - 248}{5}$

 $= (\pm) 3 \text{ μs}$

 (ii) (mean contact time $= 255 \pm 3 \text{ μs}$)

 max value $= 258 \text{ μs}$

 club does **not** meet standard

 (b) (i) $F = \dfrac{mv - mu}{t}$

 $= \dfrac{4 \cdot 5 \times 10^{-2} \times (50 - 0)}{450 \times 10^{-6}}$

 $= 5000 \text{ N}$

 (ii) Impulse on the ball is greater
 or
 Δmv is greater $\Bigg\}$
 So speed increased

23. (a) (i) $P \times V = 2000 \ 1995 \ 2002 \ 2001$
 all 4 values needed

 $P \times V = \text{constant}$

 or $P \times V = 2000$

 or $P_1 V_1 = P_2 V_2$

 or $P = k/V$

 (ii) Gas <u>molecules</u> <u>collide</u> with <u>walls</u> of container more often so (average) force increases
 pressure increases

 (b) (i) pressure due to <u>water</u>

 $\begin{aligned} P &= \rho gh \\ &= 1020 \times 9 \cdot 8 \times 12 \\ &= 120000 \text{ (Pa)} \end{aligned}$

 $\begin{aligned} \text{Total pressure} &= 120000 + 1 \cdot 01 \times 10^5 \\ &= 2 \cdot 21 \times 10^5 \text{ (Pa)} \end{aligned}$

 (ii) $P_1 V_1 = P_2 V_2$

 $1 \cdot 01 \times 10^5 \times 1 \cdot 50 \times 10^{-3} = 2 \cdot 21 \times 10^5 \times V_2$

 $V_2 = 6 \cdot 86 \times 10^{-4} \text{ m}^3$

 (c) pressure decreases as $P = \rho gh$
 volume of air in lungs will increase
 (or pressure difference increases)
 so <u>lungs</u> may become damaged

24. (a) (i) $\begin{aligned} V_{tpd} &= IR \\ &= 1 \cdot 5 \times 3 \\ &= 4 \cdot 5 \text{ (V)} \end{aligned}$

 $\begin{aligned} \text{lost volts} &= E - V_{tpd} \\ &= 6 \cdot 0 - 4 \cdot 5 \\ &= 1 \cdot 5 \text{ V} \end{aligned}$

 (ii) $r = \dfrac{\text{lost volts}}{I}$

 $= \dfrac{1 \cdot 5}{3 \cdot 0}$

 $= 0 \cdot 5 \ \Omega$

 or

 $r = \dfrac{E}{I}$

 $= \dfrac{6 \cdot 0}{12}$

 $= 0 \cdot 5 \ \Omega$

 or

 $E = IR + Ir$

 $6 \cdot 0 = (3 \times 1 \cdot 5) + (3 \times r)$

 $r = 0 \cdot 5 \ \Omega$

 (b) current decreases

 so lost volts $(V = Ir)$ decreases

25. (a) (i) $V_P = 3 \times 0.5 = 1.5$ mV

(ii) $f = \dfrac{1}{T}$

$= \dfrac{1}{4 \times 10^{-3}}$

$= 250$ Hz

(b) (i) inverting (mode)

(ii) $V_{rms} = \dfrac{V_{peak}}{\sqrt{2}}$

$= \dfrac{6.2 \times 10^{-3}}{\sqrt{2}}$

$= 4.38 \times 10^{-3}$ (V)

$\dfrac{V_O}{V_I} = -\dfrac{R_f}{R_I}$

$\dfrac{V_O}{4.38 \times 10^{-3}} = -\dfrac{10 \times 10^6}{5 \times 10^3}$

$V_O = (-)\,8.8$ V

(iii) trace will be "clipped"/flattened (at $\pm$ 9 V) or <u>almost</u> square wave

max output voltage will be $\pm$ 9 V/V_s

or op-amp saturates

or saturation occurs

26. (a) (Current)

(b) $V_R = I\,R$

$= 5 \times 10^{-3} \times 500$

$= 2.5$ (V)

$V_C = 12 - 2.5$

$= 9.5$ V

(c) $E = \dfrac{1}{2} C V^2$

$= 0.5 \times 47 \times 10^{-6} \times 12^2$

$= 3.4 \times 10^{-3}$ J

(d) Max energy the same/ 'no effect'

Values of "C" <u>and</u> "V" are same as before

27. (a) waves <u>meet</u> out of phase

or crest meets trough

or path difference $= (n + {}^1/_2)\,\lambda$

(b) $\lambda_{\text{blue light}}$ is shorter (than $\lambda_{\text{red light}}$)

and $n\,\lambda = d\,\sin\theta$

or

$\sin\theta = n\,\lambda/d$

(c) $n\,\lambda = d\,\sin\theta$

$2 \times 4.73 \times 10^{-7} = 2.00 \times 10^{-6}\,\sin\theta$

$\theta = 28.2°$

28. (a) (i) $E_3 \rightleftharpoons E_0$

$(\Delta)E \,\alpha\, f$ **or** $E = hf$

$f\,\alpha\,\dfrac{1}{\lambda}$ **or** $v = f\lambda$

(ii) $(\Delta)E = hf$ or $W_2 - W_1 = hf$

$-5.2 \times 10^{-19} - (-9.0 \times 10^{-19}) = 6.63 \times 10^{-34} \times f$

$f = 5.7 \times 10^{14}$ Hz

(b) $\lambda_a = \left(\dfrac{v}{f}\right) = \dfrac{3 \times 10^8}{4.6 \times 10^{14}}$

$= 6.5 \times 10^{-7}$ (m)

$\dfrac{\lambda_a}{\lambda_g} = \dfrac{\sin\theta_a}{\sin\theta_g}$

$\dfrac{6.5 \times 10^{-7}}{\lambda_g} = \dfrac{\sin 53°}{\sin 30°}$

$\lambda_g = 4.1 \times 10^{-7}$ m

29. (a) (i) $E_k = hf - hf_0$

$= 5.23 \times 10^{-19} - 2.56 \times 10^{-19}$

$= 2.67 \times 10^{-19}$ J

(ii) $E_k = \dfrac{1}{2} m v^2$

$2.67 \times 10^{-19} = \dfrac{1}{2} \times 9.11 \times 10^{-31} \times v^2$

$v = 7.66 \times 10^5$ ms^{-1}

(b) No change (to maximum speed)/no effect

Energy/frequency of photons does not change

or

Energy an electron receives is the same

30. (a) (i) $r = 95$

$s = 7$

(ii) Total mass of reactants

$>$ total mass of products

or

(there is a) loss of mass

(iii) Total mass before

$= 390.173 \times 10^{-27} + 1.675 \times 10^{-27}$

$= 3.91848 \times 10^{-25}$ (kg)

Total mass after

$= 230.584 \times 10^{-27} + 157.544 \times 10^{-27} +$

$(2 \times 1.675 \times 10^{-27})$

$= 3.91478 \times 10^{-25}$ (kg)

$\Delta m = 3.91848 \times 10^{-25} - 3.91478 \times 10^{-25}$

$= 3.7 \times 10^{-28}$ (kg)

$E = mc^2$

$= 3.7 \times 10^{-28} \times (3 \times 10^8)^2$

$= 3.3 \times 10^{-11}$ J

(b) (i) 12 mm

(ii) $200 \rightarrow 100 \rightarrow 50$

2 half-value thicknesses

$= 2 \times 12 = 24$ mm

PHYSICS HIGHER
2010

SECTION A

1. E	2. E	3. D	4. A
5. D	6. B	7. C	8. B
9. A	10. D	11. D	12. C
13. E	14. A	15. B	16. D
17. E	18. D	19. B	20. C

See also the extra note sheets.

SECTION B

21. (a) (i) 47 km

156$^{(o)}$

or 24° east of south

or 66° south of east

(ii) $v = s/t$

$v = (47100$ **or** $47000)/900$

$v = 52{\cdot}3$ **or** $52{\cdot}2$ m s^{-1}

[**or** 188 km h^{-1}]

at 156$^{(o)}$

(b) (i) Lift = mg **or** lift = weight

or forces balanced

$W = 1{\cdot}21 \times 10^4 \times 9{\cdot}8$

$W = 119$ kN

(ii) Weight is less

There is a resultant force upwards **or** unbalanced force upwards **or** net force upwards

Upward Acceleration

OR

The helicopter <u>accelerates upwards</u>

weight is less

there is a net upward force

22. (a) (i) The <u>total</u> momentum before (a collision) equals the <u>total</u> momentum after (the collision)

'In the absence of external forces' **or** 'in an isolated system'

(ii) $m_A u_A + m_B u_B = m_A v_A + m_B v_B$

$(0{\cdot}22 \times 0{\cdot}25) + 0{\cdot}16u = (0{\cdot}38 \times 0{\cdot}2)$

$0{\cdot}055 + 0{\cdot}16u = 0{\cdot}076$

$u = 0{\cdot}13$ m s^{-1}

(b) The find velocity is less

because the (total initial) momentum is less, the mass is constant

and v = momentum/mass

23. (a) (i) $v^2 = u^2 + 2as$

$v^2 = 0^2 + 2 \times 9{\cdot}8 \times 2$

$v = \underline{6{\cdot}3}$ (m s^{-1})

or

$(m)gh = \tfrac{1}{2}(m)v^2$

$v = \surd(2 \times 9{\cdot}8 \times 2)$

$v = \underline{6{\cdot}3}$ (m s^{-1})

(ii) $(\Delta p) = m (v - u)$

$= 40 (-5{\cdot}7 - 6.3)$

$= -480$ kg m s^{-1}

or

$(\Delta p) = m (v - u)$

$= 40 (5{\cdot}7 - (-6{\cdot}3))$

$= 480$ kg m s^{-1}

(iii) $F = \Delta p / t$

$F = (-)480/0{\cdot}5$

$F = (-)960$ N

(b) Weight/downwards force is constant

vertical component(s) balances weight

as angle increases tension must increase

because T = ½ W/ cos θ

24. (a) (i) 0·51 s

(ii) Random uncertainty = {max – min} / no.

= {0·55 – 0·49}/6

= 0·01 s

(b) (i) $Q = CV$

$Q = 1{\cdot}6 \times 10^{-3} \times 4{\cdot}5$

$Q = 7{\cdot}2 \times 10^{-3}$ C

(ii) $(I = V/R$

$I = 4{\cdot}5/18000$

$I = 0{\cdot}25$ mA)

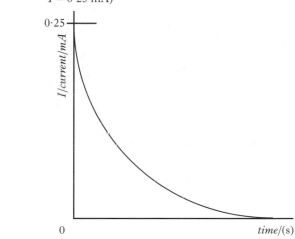

25. (a) (i) $R_1/R_2 = R_3/R_4$

$R_1 = 6000 \times 800/4000$

$R_1 = 1200\ \Omega$

(ii) $V_P = 4{\cdot}0$ V

$V_Q = 4{\cdot}8$ V

Voltmeter reading = 0·8 V

(b) $V_o = (V_2 - V_1) (R_f/R_1)$

$V_o = (3{\cdot}2 - 3{\cdot}0) (2{\cdot}0 \times 10^6/20 \times 10^3)$

$V_o = 20$ (V)

(But, due to saturation, the actual output voltage is) 10 to 12 V

26. (a) (i) $V_p = 2{\cdot}0$ V

(ii) $f = 1/T$

$f = 1/0{\cdot}01$

$f = 100$ Hz

(b) Stays the same/constant/no change/nothing

(c) increases/doubles

(d) The capacitor <u>will</u> be damaged

The peak voltage from this power supply is greater than 16 V because $V_P = \surd2 \times 15 = 21{\cdot}2$ V

27. (a) $S_2 P - S_1 P = (n + ½) \lambda$

$0{\cdot}34 = \lambda/2$

$\lambda = 0{\cdot}68$ m

or

path difference = ½ λ

path difference = 0·34 m

$\lambda = 0{\cdot}68$ m

(b) The amplitude increases **or** is greater

because <u>destructive</u> interference is no longer taking place

28. (a) (i) $P = F/A$
$F = 4 \cdot 6 \times 10^5 \times 3 \cdot 00 \times 10^{-2}$
$F = 13800$ N

(ii) $P_1 V_1 = P_2 V_2$
$4 \cdot 6 \times 10^5 \times 1 \cdot 6 \times 10^{-3} = 1 \cdot 0 \times 10^5 \times V_2$
$V_2 = 7 \cdot 36 \times 10^{-3}$ (m³)
V of water $= (7 \cdot 36 - 1 \cdot 6) \times 10^{-3}$
$= 5 \cdot 76 \times 10^{-3}$ m³

(b) (i) Stays the same/constant/nothing/no change

(ii) $n = \sin \theta_1 / \sin \theta_2$
$n = \sin 60 / \sin 41$
$n = 1 \cdot 32$

(iii) $\sin \theta_C = 1/n$
$\sin \theta_C = 1/1 \cdot 32$
$\theta_C = 49°$

(iv) The critical angle is less
because the refractive index is larger

29. (a) Very small area/diameter/radius (of beam)
$I = P/A$ **or** High irradiance

(b) $E = hf$
$E = 6 \cdot 63 \times 10^{-34} \times 4 \cdot 74 \times 10^{14}$
$E = 3 \cdot 14 \times 10^{-19}$ J

(c) Frequency/wavelength/energy
Direction
Speed
Phase/coherent
Velocity

(d) $\lambda = v/f = 3 \times 10^8 / 4 \cdot 74 \times 10^{14} = 633$ (nm)
$n\lambda = d \sin \theta$
$d = (2 \times 633 \times 10^{-9})/\sin 30$
$d = 2 \cdot 5 \times 10^{-6}$ m

30. (a) 146

(b) (i) $r = 93$
$s = 237$

(ii) $T = $ Neptunium (**or** Np)

(c) $N = At$
$N = 30 \times 10^3 \times 60$
$N = 1 \cdot 8 \times 10^6$

(d) $I = V/R$
$I = 5/16$
$I = 0 \cdot 3125$ (A)

$E = I(R + r)$
$9 = 0 \cdot 3125 (R + 2)$
$9 = 0 \cdot 3125R + 0 \cdot 625$
$8 \cdot 375 = 0 \cdot 3125R$
$R = 26 \cdot 8$ Ω

$R = 26 \cdot 8 - 16 = 10 \cdot 8 = 11$ Ω

or

$I = V/R$
$I = 5/16$
$I = 0 \cdot 3125$ (A)

$V_{lost} = Ir = 2 \times 0 \cdot 3125 = 0 \cdot 625$ (V)

$V_{resistor} = 9 - (5 + 0 \cdot 625) = 3 \cdot 375$ (V)

$R = V/I$
$R = 3 \cdot 375/0 \cdot 3125$
$R = 10 \cdot 8 = 11$Ω

or

$I = V/R$
$= 5/16$
$= 0 \cdot 3125$ (A)

$R_T = E/I$
$= 9/0 \cdot 3125$
$= 28 \cdot 8$Ω

$R = R_T - 18 = 28.8 - 18$
$= 10 \cdot 8 = 11$Ω

PHYSICS HIGHER 2011

SECTION A

1. C	2. E	3. C	4. A
5. C	6. D	7. A	8. E
9. C	10. B	11. B	12. A
13. D	14. E	15. D	16. B
17. D	18. A	19. B	20. A

SECTION B

21. (a) (i) $v^2 = u^2 + 2as$

$0 = 7^2 + 2 \times (-9 \cdot 8) \times s$

$s = \textbf{2·5}$ m

or

$v = u + at$

$0 = 7 + (-9 \cdot 8) t$

$t = 0 \cdot 71$ s

$s = ut + \frac{1}{2} a t^2$

$= 7 \times 0 \cdot 71 + \frac{1}{2} (-9 \cdot 8)(0 \cdot 71)^2$

$= \textbf{2·5}$ m

(ii) $v = u + at$

$0 = 7 + (-9 \cdot 8) \times t$

$t = \textbf{0·71}$ s

or

$s = \left(\frac{u + v}{2}\right) t$

$2 \cdot 5 = \left(\frac{7 + 0}{2}\right) \times t$

$t = \textbf{0·71}$ s

(b) (i) $1 \cdot 5$ m s^{-1} to the **right**

(ii) Statement Z

Horizontal speed of ball remains constant and equal to (horizontal) speed of trolley

or

Horizontal speed of the ball remains constant at $1 \cdot 5$ m s^{-1}

22. (a) (i) *Impulse = Area under F–t graph*

$= \frac{1}{2} 6 \cdot 4 \times 0 \cdot 25$

$= \textbf{0·80}$ kg m s^{-1}

(ii) **0·80** kg m s^{-1}

in the negative direction **or** to the left

(iii) *(Impulse = Change in momentum)*

$F \times t = mv - mu$

$-0 \cdot 80 = m(-0 \cdot 45 - 0 \cdot 48)$

$m = \textbf{0·86}$ kg

(b)

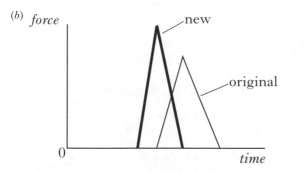

23. (a) (i) $m = 111 \cdot 49 - 111 \cdot 26$

$= 0 \cdot 23$ g

$\rho = m/V$

$= 0 \cdot 23 \times 10^{-3}/2 \cdot 0 \times 10^{-4}$

$= \textbf{1·15}$ kg m^{-3}

(ii) Not all the air will be evacuated from jar

or

It is impossible to get a (perfect) vacuum

or

Some air has leaked back in

(b) (i) $P_1 V_1 = P_2 V_2$

$1 \cdot 01 \times 10^5 \times 200 = P_2 \times 250$

$P_2 = \textbf{8·1} \times 10^4$ Pa

(ii) Particles <u>collide</u> with <u>walls</u> of jar

So when air is removed, number of collisions on walls of jar is less frequent/less often and average force (on walls) decreases, and pressure on walls of jar decreases

24. (a) (i) 10 joules of energy are given to each coulomb (of charge) passing through the supply

(ii) $I = \dfrac{E}{(R + r)}$

$1 \cdot 25 = \dfrac{10}{(6 + r)}$

$r = \textbf{2·0}\ \Omega$

or

$r = \dfrac{lost\ volts}{I}$

$= \dfrac{10 - 7 \cdot 5}{1 \cdot 25}$

$= \textbf{2·0}\ \Omega$

or

$\dfrac{R_1}{R_2} = \dfrac{V_1}{V_2}$

$\dfrac{r}{6 \cdot 0} = \dfrac{2 \cdot 5}{7 \cdot 5}$

$r = \textbf{2·0}\ \Omega$

(b) (i) (Total) resistance decreases (circuit) current increases lost volts increases

(ii) Parallel resistance $= R = V/I$

$= 6 \cdot 0/2 \cdot 0$

$= 3 \cdot 0\ \Omega$

$1/R_T = 1/R_1 + 1/R_2$

$1/3 = 1/6 + 1/R$

$R = \textbf{6·0}\ \Omega$

or

Total resistance $= E/I$

$= 10/2 \cdot 0$

$= 5 \cdot 0\ \Omega$

Resistance of parallel network $= 5 - 2$

$= 3\ \Omega$

$R_T = \dfrac{Product}{Sum}$

$3 = \dfrac{6 \times R}{6 + R}$

$R = \textbf{6·0}\ \Omega$

25. (a) 200 µC of charge increases voltage across plates by 1 volt

or

200 µC per volt

or

One volt across the plates of the capacitor causes 200 µC of charge to be stored

(b) (i) $I = E/R$

$\quad = 12/1400$

$\quad = \mathbf{0{\cdot}0086}$ **A**

$\qquad (\mathbf{8{\cdot}6\ mA})$

(ii) $E = \frac{1}{2}\,CV^2$

initial stored energy $= \frac{1}{2} \times (200 \times 10^{-6}) \times 12^2$

$\qquad = 0{\cdot}0144$ J

final stored energy $= \frac{1}{2}(200 \times 10^{-6}) \times 4^2$

$\qquad = 0{\cdot}0016$ J

Difference $= 0{\cdot}0144 - 0{\cdot}0016$

decrease in stored energy $= \mathbf{0{\cdot}0128}$ J

(c) (i) $0{\cdot}30$ s

(ii) $s = ut + \frac{1}{2}\,a\,t^2$

$0{\cdot}80 = 1{\cdot}5 \times 0{\cdot}3 + \frac{1}{2} \times a \times (0{\cdot}3)^2$

$a = \mathbf{7{\cdot}8}$ **m s^{-2}**

(iii) Percentage (fractional) uncertainty in (measuring) <u>distance</u> will be smaller

or

Percentage (fractional) uncertainty in (measuring) <u>time</u> will be smaller

26. (a) (i) Inverting

(ii) $V_o = -\dfrac{R_f}{R_1} \times V_1$

$12 = \dfrac{-80}{10} \times V_1$

$V_1 = -\mathbf{1{\cdot}5}$ **V**

(iii) Output cannot be greater than (approx 85% of) the supply voltage

or

Saturation <u>of the amplifier</u> has been reached

(b)

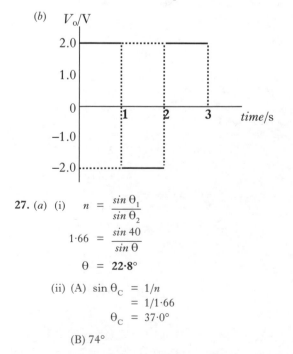

27. (a) (i) $n = \dfrac{\sin\theta_1}{\sin\theta_2}$

$1{\cdot}66 = \dfrac{\sin 40}{\sin\theta}$

$\theta = \mathbf{22{\cdot}8}°$

(ii) (A) $\sin\theta_C = 1/n$

$\qquad\quad = 1/1{\cdot}66$

$\theta_C = 37{\cdot}0°$

(B) 74°

(b) No

or

it is totally internally reflected }

and

n depends on frequency

or

$n_{\text{blue}} > n_{\text{red}}$

or

blue refracts more than red }

and

(critical angle)$_{\text{blue}}$ < (critical angle)$_{\text{red}}$

or

the angle of incidence has increased }

and

angle of incidence of blue light on face PQ is greater than the critical angle

28. (a) Light travels as waves

or

Energy in light is carried as a wave

or

Light is a wave

(b) (i) $d\sin\theta = n\lambda$

$5 \times 10^{-6} \times \sin 11 = 2 \times \lambda$

$\lambda = \mathbf{480}$ nm

(ii) Spacing of maxima increases

λ in liquid increases

(as n decreases)

$\sin\theta = n\lambda/d$

θ increases

29. (a) (i) $f = \dfrac{c}{\lambda}$

$\quad = \dfrac{3{\cdot}00 \times 10^8}{525 \times 10^{-9}}$

$\quad = 5{\cdot}71 \times 10^{14}$ Hz

$E = hf$

$\quad = 6{\cdot}63 \times 10^{-34} \times 5{\cdot}71 \times 10^{14}$

$\quad = \mathbf{3{\cdot}79 \times 10^{-19}}$ **J**

(ii) $\left(\begin{array}{l} E_k = hf - hf_o \\ \quad = 3{\cdot}79 \times 10^{-19} - 2{\cdot}24 \times 10^{-19} \end{array} \right)$

$= \mathbf{1{\cdot}55 \times 10^{-19}}$ **J**

(b) (i) <u>Photons</u> with frequency below f_o do not have enough <u>energy</u> to release electrons

or

<u>Photons</u> with frequency below f_o have <u>energy</u> smaller than work function

(ii) Work function $= hf_o$ (**or** $E = hf_o$)

$2{\cdot}24 \times 10^{-19} = (6{\cdot}63 \times 10^{-34}) \times f_o$

$f_o = \mathbf{3{\cdot}38 \times 10^{14}}$ **Hz**

30. (a) (i) (Nuclear) Fusion

(ii) Total mass before

$= 3{\cdot}342 \times 10^{-27} + 5{\cdot}005 \times 10^{-27}$

$= 8{\cdot}347 \times 10^{-27}$ (kg)

Total mass after

$= 6{\cdot}642 \times 10^{-27} + 1{\cdot}675 \times 10^{-27}$

$$= 8 \cdot 317 \times 10^{-27} \text{ (kg)}$$

Loss in mass $= 0 \cdot 030 \times 10^{-27}$ (kg)

Energy released $= mc^2$

$$= 0 \cdot 030 \times 10^{-27} \times (3 \cdot 00 \times 10^8)^2$$

$$= \mathbf{2 \cdot 7 \times 10^{-12}} \text{ J}$$

(b) (i) Energy absorbed

$$= -1 \cdot 360 \times 10^{-19} - (-5 \cdot 424 \times 10^{-19})$$

$$= 4 \cdot 064 \times 10^{-19} (\text{J})$$

$$E = hf$$

$$4 \cdot 064 \times 10^{-19} = 6 \cdot 63 \times 10^{-34} \times f$$

$$f = 6 \cdot 13 \times 10^{14} \text{ (Hz)}$$

$$\lambda = \frac{c}{f}$$

$$= \frac{3 \cdot 00 \times 10^8}{6 \cdot 13 \times 10^{14}}$$

$$= \mathbf{489} \text{ nm}$$

(ii) 'Blue' **or** 'blue-green'

PHYSICS HIGHER 2012

SECTION A

1. E	**2.** A	**3.** C	**4.** C
5. C	**6.** D	**7.** B	**8.** D
9. B	**10.** C	**11.** B	**12.** E
13. D	**14.** E	**15.** D	**16.** A
17. A	**18.** D	**19.** B	**20.** B

SECTION B

21. (a) (i) North

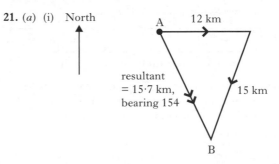

($\frac{1}{2}$) for correct diagram to scale, length and angle
($\frac{1}{2}$) for adding correctly showing resultant direction (arrow needed)

displacement $= 15 \cdot 7 \pm 0 \cdot 3$ km

bearing $= 154 \pm 2$ (26° E of S)
(64° S of E)

(ii) $v = \dfrac{s}{t}$

$$= \frac{15 \cdot 7}{1 \cdot 25}$$

$$= 12 \cdot 6 \text{ km h}^{-1} \text{ at } 154$$

(b) (i) $15 \cdot 7$ km on a bearing of 154

(ii) $t = \dfrac{d}{v}$

$$= \frac{33}{22}$$

$$= 1 \cdot 5 \text{ hours}$$

$$v = \frac{s}{t}$$

$$= \frac{15 \cdot 7}{1 \cdot 5}$$

$$= 10 \cdot 5 \text{ km h}^{-1} \text{ on a bearing of } 154$$

22. (a) (i) $d = vt$
$$= 20 \times 3 \cdot 06$$
$$= 61 \cdot 2 \text{ m}$$

(ii) $v^2 = u^2 + 2as$
$$0 = 15^2 + 2 \times -9 \cdot 8 \times s$$
$$s = 11 \cdot 5 \text{ m}$$
$$(11 \cdot 48)$$

(b) More likely, because:

horizontal velocity will decrease
range will decrease
time in air will decrease
height reached will decrease

23. (a) (i) $E_w = Q V$
$= 1\cdot6 \times 10^{-19} \times 1220$
$= 1\cdot95 \times 10^{-16}$ J

(ii) work done $= \frac{1}{2} mv^2$
$= \frac{1}{2} \times 2\cdot18 \times 10^{-25} \times v^2$
$v = 4\cdot23 \times10^4$ m s^{-1}

(b) $Ft = \Delta mv$
$0\cdot07 \times 60 = 750 \times \Delta v$
$\Delta v = 5\cdot6 \times 10^{-3}$ m s^{-1}

(c) Force from Xenon engine greater

Change in momentum of the Xenon ions would be greater (than Krypton ions)

Impulse from Xenon ions would be greater

24. (a)

P/T	347	347	346	348	348

Pressure and temperature (in K) are directly proportional

(b) As temperature increases, E_k of gas molecules/particles increases (**or** molecules travel faster) and hit/collide with the walls of the container more often/frequently

with greater force

pressure increases

(c) To ensure all the gas in the flask is heated evenly

or all the gas is at the same temperature

25. (a) (i) $I = \dfrac{E}{(R + r)}$
$= \dfrac{12}{(6 + 2)}$
$= 1\cdot5$ A

(ii) $V = Ir$
$= 1\cdot5 \times 2$
$= 3\cdot0$ V

(iii) $P = I^2R$
$= (1\cdot5)^2 \times 6$
$= 13\cdot5$ W
or
$P = V^2/R$
$= 9^2/6$
$= 13\cdot5$ W
or
$P = IV$
$= 1\cdot5 \times 9$
$= 13\cdot5$ W

(b) $P = I^2R$
(Circuit) current increases
Total or circuit resistance decreases
Internal resistance less
or
$P = V^2/R$
Voltage across lamp increases
Lost volts decreases
Internal resistance less

26. (a)

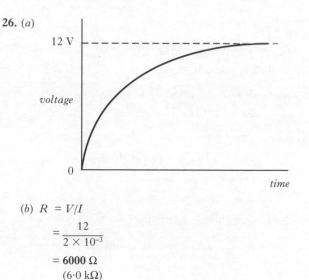

(b) $R = V/I$
$= \dfrac{12}{2 \times 10^{-3}}$
$= 6000\ \Omega$
$(6\cdot0$ k$\Omega)$

(c) (i) Initial current only depends on the values of the e.m.f. of the supply <u>and</u> resistor R which do not change.

(ii) Smaller
Capacitor takes less time to discharge

27. (a) Resistance of fabric $= 40\ \Omega$

$\dfrac{R_1}{R_2} = \dfrac{R_3}{R_4}$

$\dfrac{R_V}{40} = \dfrac{240}{80}$

$R_V = 120\ \Omega$

(b) (i) Differential Mode

(ii) Gain $= \dfrac{R_f}{R_l}$
$= \dfrac{560}{100}$
$= 5\cdot6$

(iii) (A) Gain $= \dfrac{V_{out}}{V_{in}}$
$5\cdot6 = \dfrac{10\cdot8}{V_{in}}$
$V_{in} = 1\cdot93$ V

(B) Potential at X $= 2\cdot25 + 1\cdot93$
$= 4\cdot18$ V

$\dfrac{R_1}{R_2} = \dfrac{V_1}{V_2}$

$\dfrac{R_1}{120} = \dfrac{4\cdot18}{4\cdot82}$

$R_1 = 104\ \Omega$
Length of fabric $= 66$ mm

28. (a) $n = \dfrac{sin\ \theta_1}{sin\ \theta_2}$

$1\cdot33 = \dfrac{sin\ X}{sin\ 36}$

X $= 51°$

(b) (i) Angle of refraction is 90°
or
Refracted ray makes an angle of 90° with normal
or
Refracted ray is along surface of water

(ii) $\sin \theta_C = 1/n$

$\qquad = 1/1\cdot33$

$\qquad \theta_C = \mathbf{49°}$

(c)

Totally internally reflected ray shown (angles should be equal)

29. (a) $\qquad dsin\theta = n\lambda$

$d \times sin\ 35\cdot3 = 3 \times 633 \times 10^{-9}$

$d = \mathbf{3\cdot29 \times 10^{-6}\ m}$

(b) Number of lines per metre $= \dfrac{1}{3\cdot29 \times 10^{-6}}$

$\qquad\qquad = \mathbf{3\cdot04 \times 10^{5}}$

(c) $\qquad$ Difference $= (3\cdot04 - 3\cdot00) \times 10^{5}$

$\qquad\qquad = 0\cdot04 \times 10^{5}$

Percentage difference $= \dfrac{0\cdot04 \times 10^{5}}{3\cdot00 \times 10^{5}} \times 100$

$\qquad\qquad = 1\cdot33\%$

Technician's value does agree

30. (a) Decreases

(b) (i) Photoconductive mode

(ii) Current increases

more photons of light arrive at the junction per second

more free charge carriers produced per second

(c) $\qquad I_1\ d_1{}^2 = I_2\ d_2{}^2$

$3\cdot0 \times 10^{-6} \times 1\cdot2^2 = I_2 \times 0\cdot8^2$

$\qquad\qquad I_2 = 6\cdot75\ \mu A$

31. (a) $\qquad D = \dfrac{E}{m}$

$500 \times 10^{-6} = \dfrac{E}{0\cdot04}$

$\qquad E = 2\cdot0 \times 10^{-5}\ J$

(b) $\qquad \dot{H} = \dfrac{H}{t}$

$5\cdot0 \times 10^{-3} = \dfrac{H}{2}$

$\qquad H = 0\cdot01\ (Sv)$

$\qquad H = Dw_R$

$0\cdot01 = 500 \times 10^{-6} \times w_R$

$\qquad w_R = 20$

alpha radiation

SECTION A

1. E	2. B	3. B	4. A
5. C	6. A	7. C	8. E
9. D	10. E	11. D	12. B
13. E	14. A	15. B	16. D
17. B	18. C	19. D	20. D

SECTION B

21. (a) $v = u + at$

$20 = 0 + 4a$

$a = 5\cdot0\ m\ s^{-2}$

(b)

car	motorcycle
$d = v \times t$	$s = ut + \frac{1}{2}\ at^2$
$d = 15 \times 4$	$s = \frac{1}{2} \times 5 \times 16$
$d = 60$	$s = 40$

Extra distance $= 60 - 40$

$\qquad\qquad = 20\ m$

(c) (i) $F_{(resultant)} = ma$

$F_{(resultant)} = 290 \times 5$

$F_{(resultant)} = 1450\ (N)$

Frictional force $= 1450 - 1800$

$\qquad\qquad = (-)350\ N$

(ii) The *faster it goes*, the greater the *air resistance*.

$\qquad$ **or** *frictional forces / friction / drag*

If $F_{(drive)}$ constant, the unbalanced force would decrease

or

increasing $F_{(drive)}$ keeps the unbalanced force constant

22. (a) $s = ut + \frac{1}{2}\ at^2$

$s = 0 + \frac{1}{2} \times -9\cdot8 \times \mathbf{0\cdot50^2}$

$s = -1\cdot225\ m$

height above ground $= 2\cdot5 - 1\cdot225$

$\qquad\qquad = 1\cdot275\ m$

(b) At impact, vertical velocity:

$v^2 = u^2 + 2as$

$v^2 = 0 + 2 \times -9\cdot8 \times -2\cdot5$

$v = 7\ (m\ s^{-1})$

horizontal velocity:

$v = 24\ (m\ s^{-1})$

resultant velocity:

$v^2\ = 49 + 576$ (by Pythagoras)

$v\ = 25\ m\ s^{-1}$

$tan\ \theta = 7/24$

$\theta = 16\cdot26°\qquad = 16°$ to the horizontal

(c) (As the temperature increases,)

the E_k/v of the molecules increases/is greater

Molecules more collisions <u>per second</u> with the walls

and they collide with a greater force/harder/more violently

so pressure increases

23. (a) <u>total</u> momentum before a <u>collision</u> is equal to <u>total</u> momentum after collision, in the absence of external forces

(b) $\Delta mv = mv - mu$

$\Delta mv = 1200 \times 0 - 1200 \times 13\cdot4$

$\Delta mv = -16080$ kg m s^{-1}

$\Delta mv = -1\cdot6 \times 10^4$ kg m s^{-1}

(c) $v^2 = u^2 + 2as$

$0 = 13\cdot4^2 + 2 \times a \times 0\cdot48$

$a = -187\cdot04$ m s^{-2}

$F = ma$

$F = 75 \times (-)187\cdot04$

$F = (-)14\,028$ N

$F = 1\cdot4 \times 10^4$ N

24. (a) $P = F/A$

$1\cdot01 \times 10^5 = 262/A$

$A = 2\cdot59 \times 10^{-3}$ m^2

(b) (i) $\Delta P = 513\,000 - 1\cdot01 \times 10^5$
$\Delta P = 412\,000$ Pa
$(\Delta)P = \rho g h$
$412\,000 = 1\cdot02 \times 10^3 \times 9\cdot8 \times h$
Depth $h = 41\cdot2$ m

(ii) Volume increases because,
P decreases
or $P \propto 1/V$
or PV = const.

(c) Voltage at inverting input is 12 V, or $V_1 = 12$ V

$V_2 = 6$ V

$V_o = (V_2 - V_1) \times \dfrac{R_f}{R_i}$

$V_o = (6 - 12) \times \dfrac{150 \times 10^3}{50 \times 10^3}$

$= -18$ (V)

(Op-amp saturates at a maximum)
V_o of -15V

25. (a) (i) 0·22 V

(ii) $E = V + Ir$

$0\cdot22 = 0\cdot10 + 3r$

$r = 0\cdot04\ \Omega$

or

$E = I(R + r)$

$0\cdot22 = 0\cdot5\ (0\cdot4 + r)$

$r = 0\cdot04\ \Omega$

(b) $E = I(R + r)$

$0\cdot88 = I\ (0\cdot12 + 0\cdot15)$

$I = 3\cdot26$ A

Yes

26. (a) total time = no. of divisions × time base setting
$= 10 \times 0\cdot01$
$= 0\cdot1$ (s)
$f = \dfrac{\text{number of waves}}{\text{total time}}$

$= \dfrac{2.5}{0.1}$

$= 25$ Hz

(b) $V_p = \sqrt{2}\ V_{rms}$
$= \sqrt{2} \times 2\cdot30$
$= 3\cdot25$ V

(c) Stays constant/
<u>Current</u> is independent of supply frequency

27. (a) (i) $V = IR$

$250 = I \times 15\,000$

$I = 17$ mA

(ii)

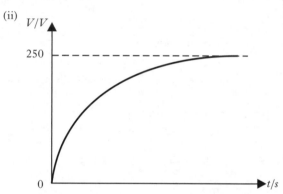

(iii) $E = \frac{1}{2}\ CV^2$

$= \frac{1}{2} \times 470 \times 10^{-6} \times 250^2$

$= 14\cdot7$ J

(b) $P = \dfrac{E}{t}$

$= \dfrac{14\cdot7}{200 \times 10^{-6}}$

$= 73\,500$ W

(c) Reduce the value of the resistor.

28. (a) (i) waves <u>meet</u> out of phase
or
crests <u>meet</u> troughs

(ii) Path difference $= n\lambda$

p.d. $= 3 \times 28 \times 10^{-3}$

p.d. $= 84$ (mm)

distance from S_2 to P $= 620 + 84$

S_2 to P $= 704$ mm

(b) $n\lambda = d\sin\theta$

$n \times 420 \times 10^{-9} = 3 \cdot 27 \times 10^{-6} \times \sin 40$

$n = 5$

total no. of maxima = 5 above + 5 below + central

= 11

29. (a) $n = \sin\theta_1 / \sin\theta_2$

$1 \cdot 49 = \sin\theta_{air} / \sin 19$

$\theta_{air} = 29°$

(b) $n = 1/\sin\theta_c$

$1 \cdot 49 = 1/\sin\theta_c$

$\theta_c = 42°$

(c) Different frequencies/colours are <u>refracted</u> through different angles

or

The <u>refractive index</u> is different for different frequencies/colours

30. (a) $I_1 d_1^2 = I_2 d_2^2$

$242 \times 0 \cdot 10^2 = 242 \times 10^{-2}$
$106 \times 0 \cdot 15^2 = 239 \times 10^{-2}$
$60 \times 0 \cdot 20^2 = 240 \times 10^{-2}$
$39 \times 0 \cdot 25^2 = 244 \times 10^{-2}$

All values of Id^2 are about the same

So it <u>is</u> a point source

(b) (i) laser beam does not diverge
or laser is not a point source (of light)
or reading is high because laser light is concentrated on a small area

(ii) $v = f\lambda$
$3 \cdot 0 \times 10^8 = f \times 633 \times 10^{-9}$
$f = 4 \cdot 74 \times 10^{14}$

$E = hf$
$= 6 \cdot 63 \times 10^{-34} \times 4 \cdot 74 \times 10^{14}$
$= 3 \cdot 142 \times 10^{-19}$

$\text{Number of photons} = \dfrac{\text{total energy}}{\text{photon energy}}$

$= \dfrac{1 \cdot 00 \times 10^{-4}}{3 \cdot 142 \times 10^{-19}}$

$= 3 \cdot 18 \times 10^{14}$

(iii) for laser light:
photons have same frequency, energy, wavelength
all photons are in phase
or
for lamp:
photons have a range of frequencies
photons are not in phase

31 .(a) (i) Lithium

(ii) $E = mc^2$

$2 \cdot 97 \times 10^{-12} = m \times (3 \times 10^8)^2$

$m = 0 \cdot 033 \times 10^{-27}$ (kg)

$\times + 3 \cdot 342 \times 10^{-27} =$

$(2 \times 6 \cdot 642 + 1 \cdot 675 + 0 \cdot 033) \times 10^{-27}$

$\times = 11 \cdot 650 \times 10^{-27}$ kg

(b) $\dot{H} = \dot{D}w_R$

$= (2 \times 1) + (1 \cdot 25 \times 2) + (0 \cdot 2 \times 10)$

$\dot{H} = 6 \cdot 5 \; \mu\text{Sv h}^{-1}$
so, $H = 12 \times 6 \cdot 5$
$= \textbf{78} \; \boldsymbol{\mu}\textbf{Sv}$